Level 5

Opening Doors

Reading and Writing Activity Book

Linda Ventriglia, Ph.D.

Santillana USA
www.santillanausa.com

© 2003 Santillana USA Publishing Company, Inc.
2105 NW 86th Avenue
Miami, FL 33122

Acknowledgments

Page 75: "The River" is adapted from the poem "Where Go the Boats?," by Robert Louis Stevenson. "Where Go the Boats?" appears in *A Child's Garden of Verses*, published by C. Scribner's Sons.

Page 95: "The Road Not Taken," from *The Poetry of Robert Frost*. Reprinted as appears in the version published by Henry Holt and Co.

Pages 115-116: "Columbus" from *Songs of the Soul*, by Joaquin Miller. Reprinted as appears in the version published by Whitaker & Ray.

Pages 201-202: *How We Made the First Flight*, by Orville Wright. Reprinted as appears in the version published by the Federal Aviation Administration and the Smithsonian Institute.

Opening Doors, Level 5
ISBN: 1-58986-558-8

Editorial: Imperial Communications
Art: Bill Dickson, Contact Jupiter
Layout and cover design: Noreen T. Shimano

04 05 06   5 4 3

Printed in Colombia by Panamericana Formas e Impresos S.A.

Santillana USA
www.santillanausa.com

Our mission is to make learning and teaching English and Spanish an experience that is motivating, enriching, and effective for both teachers and students. Our goal is to satisfy the diverse needs of our customers. By involving authors, editors, teachers and students, we produce innovative and pedagogically sound materials that make use of the latest technological advances. We help to develop people's creativity. We bring ideas and imagination into education.

CONTENTS

Name _____   Date _____

a Asking and Answering Questions

■ Ask and answer the questions with a partner.

What's his name? <u>His name is Jamal.</u>
His address is <u>20 East Franklin Street,</u>
       <u>Philadelphia, Pennsylvania.</u>

What's his name? _____

His address is _____

_____

What's her name? _____

Her address is _____

_____

Sara
5 Einstein Way
Orlando, Florida

What's her name? _____

Her address is _____

_____

What's your name and address? <u>My name is</u> _____

My address is _____

ELD Standard
    Ask and answer questions using phrases or simple sentences.
ELA Standard
    Ask questions that seek information not already discussed.

Name _____   Date _____

b Word Families, Spelling Friends _ame, _ail

same   name   flame   blame   frame

fail   tail   mail   rail   snail

■ Write the correct word in each sentence. Then read the sentences to a partner.

1. Put the picture in the _____.

2. The mailman is going to give me the _____.

3. The boys are twins. They look the _____.

4. The girl didn't study for her test. She might _____.

5. My _____ is Adam. What's your name?

6. Don't _____ me for being late.

7. The freight train travels on a _____.

8. Did you see how slowly the _____ moves?

9. The cat has a very long _____.

10. The _____ on the candle was bright.

ELD Standard
Recognize English phonemes that correspond to phonemes students already hear and produce while reading aloud.
Begin to speak with a few words or sentences, using some English phonemes and rudimentary English grammatical forms.
ELA Standard
Spell roots, suffixes, prefixes, contractions, and syllable constructions correctly.

Name _____   Date _____

ⓐ Writing Sentences

- Write a sentence, using an action verb, which describes what each person is doing.
- Underline the action verb in each sentence.
- Read the sentences to a partner.

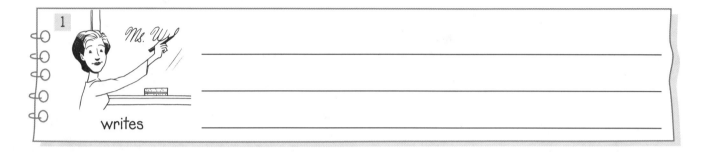

1   writes

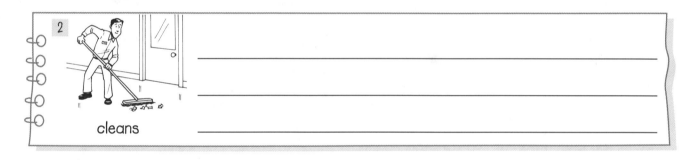

2   cleans

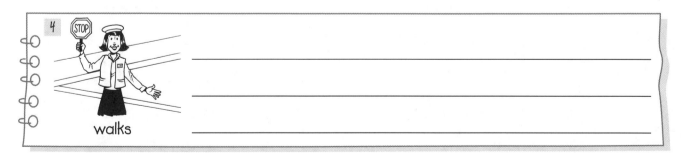

3   types

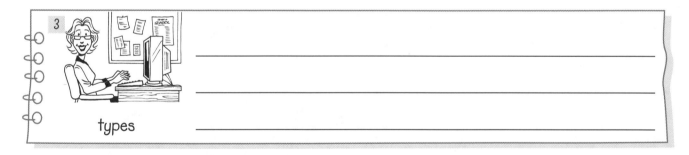

4   walks

ELD Standard
    Create simple sentences or phrases with some assistance.
ELA Standard
    Identify and correctly use verbs that are often misused, modifiers, and pronouns.

Name _____   Date _____

b Word Families, Spelling Friends _ain, _ay

■ Review the meaning of each word in the following chart.

| 1 rain | 2 pain | 3 stain | 4 train |
| 5 hay | 6 ray | 7 lay | 8 play |

■ Read the words in the box.

■ Write a sentence for each word in the box.

1. _____

2. _____

3. _____

4. _____

5. _____

6. _____

7. _____

8. _____

Name _____   Date _____

a Asking and Answering Questions

■ Read each expression in the box.

Please give me the _____.	Excuse me.	Please pass me the _____.
Thank you.	May I try on the _____?	Good morning.
	You're welcome.	

■ Respond to each situation with the correct expression.

1

You step on a six-foot-tall basketball player's foot.
He looks down at you with a frown. What do you say?

_____

2

You are eating pizza with friends. The friends are eating all the pizza.
There is no pizza at your end of the table. You want the friends to
pass you the pizza. What do you say?

_____

3

It is early morning. You are walking your dog.
You meet a lady walking her dog. What do you say?

_____

4

Your aunt gives you a new bike for your birthday.
What do you say?

_____

5

You are at the shoe store, looking for a new pair of tennis shoes.
You want to try on the high top tennis shoes. What do you say?

_____

6

You want the librarian to give you a book.
What do you say?

_____

7

You give the ball to a friend. The friend says, "Thank you."
What do you say?

_____

ELD Standard
   Ask and answer questions using phrases or simple sentences. Use common social greetings.
ELA Standard
   Ask questions that seek information not already discussed.

Name _____   Date _____

b Word Families, Spelling Friends _eet, _eep, _eed

■ Review the meaning of each word in the following chart.

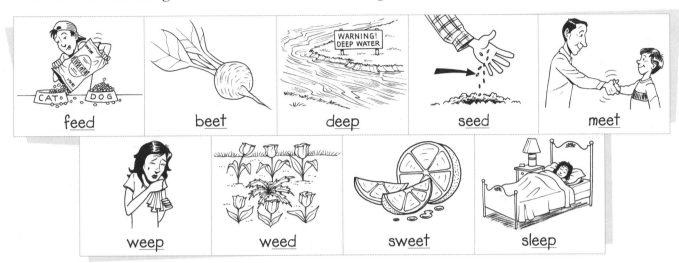

feed   beet   deep   seed   meet

weep   weed   sweet   sleep

■ Read the words above.

■ Write the correct word in each sentence.

■ Read the sentences to a partner.

1. Did you _____ the new teacher?

2. Pull the _____ from the garden.

3. The river's water is very _____.

4. The orange tastes very _____.

5. A _____ is a vegetable.

6. She is very sad. She starts to _____.

7. Everyday I _____ my cat and dog.

8. At night, I go to bed and _____.

9. Plant the _____ in the ground.

ELD Standard
Recognize English phonemes that correspond to phonemes students already hear and produce while reading aloud.
Begin to speak with a few words or sentences, using some English phonemes and rudimentary English grammatical forms.
ELA Standard
Spell roots, suffixes, prefixes, contractions, and syllable constructions correctly.

Name _____   Date _____

a Creating Word Maps

- Create word maps.

Picture A

library

Picture B

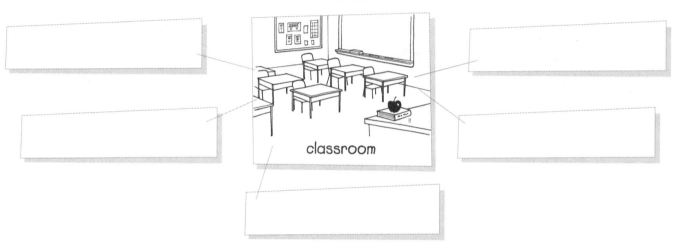

classroom

Picture C

cafeteria

■ Create three sentences for each picture, using the words on your word map.
Ask and answer the questions with a partner.

Picture A   What can you find in a library?

1. You can find a _____ in a library.

What can you find in a library?

2. _____

What can you find in a library?

3. _____

Picture B   What can you use in a classroom?

1. You can use a _____ in a classroom.

What can you use in a classroom?

2. _____

What can you use in a classroom?

3. _____

Picture C   What can you eat in a cafeteria?

1. You can eat a _____ in the cafeteria.

What can you eat in a cafeteria?

2. _____

What can you eat in a cafeteria?

3. _____

ELD Standard
  Ask and answer questions using phrases or simple sentences. Write an increasing number of words and simple
  sentences appropriate for language arts and other content areas.
ELA Standard
  Understand how text features (e.g., format, graphics, sequence, diagrams, illustrations, charts, maps) make information
  accessible and usable.

9

Name _____   Date _____

b Word Families, Spelling Friends _eat, _eak

■ Review the meaning of each word on the following chart.

| 1 meat | 2 seat | 3 pleat | 4 wheat |
| 5 beak | 6 peak | 7 leak | 8 squeak |

■ Read the words in the box.

■ Write a sentence for each word.

■ Read the sentences to a partner.

1. _____

2. _____

3. _____

4. _____

5. _____

6. _____

7. _____

8. _____

ELD Standard
Recognize English phonemes that correspond to phonemes students already hear and produce while reading aloud.
Begin to speak with a few words or sentences, using some English phonemes and rudimentary English grammatical forms.
ELA Standard
Spell roots, suffixes, prefixes, contractions, and syllable constructions correctly.

10

Name   Date

a Demonstrating Comprehension

Playground Rules

It is important to remember safety rules when you are on the playground. Here are the rules you should follow:

1. Take turns using the tetherball.
2. Do not run on the blacktop.
3. Freeze when the bell rings.
4. Do not push people.
5. Do not go into the street after the ball.

1. The rules tell you how to —
   - [ ] play a game of basketball
   - [ ] ride a bike
   - [ ] be safe
   - [ ] read a book

2. Which of these is one way to follow rule #5?
   - [ ] Keep the ball out of the street.
   - [ ] Keep running when the bell rings.
   - [ ] Don't run to class.
   - [ ] Don't push.

3. What should you <u>not</u> do when the bell rings?
   - [ ] wait quietly
   - [ ] play hopscotch
   - [ ] freeze
   - [ ] stand still

4. Another good title for this article is
   - [ ] The Big Ball
   - [ ] Tetherball Rules
   - [ ] Running at School
   - [ ] Recess Safety Rules

ELD Standard
   Read grade appropriate narrative and expository texts aloud with appropriate pacing, intonation, and expression.
ELA Standard
   Discern main ideas and concepts presented in text, identifying and assessing evidence that supports those ideas.

Name _____   Date _____

b Word Families, Spelling Friends _eal, _each

▪ Review the meaning of each word on the following chart.

| 1 meal | 2 seal | 3 steal | 4 squeal |
| 5 teach | 6 beach | 7 peach | 8 reach |

▪ Read the words in the box.
▪ Write a sentence for each word.
▪ Read the sentences to a partner.

1. _____

2. _____

3. _____

4. _____

5. _____

6. _____

7. _____

8. _____

Name _____   Date _____

a Demonstrating Listening Comprehension

How to Make a School Lunch

You will need:

2 slices of bread
2 pieces of ham
1 teaspoon mayonnaise
1 knife
1 sandwich bag
1 apple
2 cookies

1. Put the two pieces of ham on one slice of bread.
2. Put the piece of cheese on top of the ham.
3. Spread the mayonnaise on the second slice of bread with a knife.
4. Put the second slice of bread on top of the ham.
5. Put the sandwich in the sandwich bag.
6. Put the apple and cookies in the lunchbox.
7. Put the sandwich in the lunchbox.

1. When you make a ham and cheese sandwich, the knife is used to —
   - [ ] stir the mayonnaise
   - [ ] cook the ham
   - [ ] cut the cookies
   - [ ] spread the mayonnaise

2. This school lunch does <u>not</u> have the following in it —
   - [ ] milk
   - [ ] apple
   - [ ] sandwich
   - [ ] cookies

3. After you spread the mayonnaise on the second slice of bread, you —
   - [ ] take the lunchbox to school with you
   - [ ] put the second slice of bread on top of the ham
   - [ ] eat the sandwich
   - [ ] put the sandwich in the sandwich bag

4. This article was written to —
   - [ ] describe a person
   - [ ] tell about a place
   - [ ] tell you how to do something
   - [ ] sell you a ticket

ELD Standard
Apply knowledge of content-related vocabulary to discussions and reading. Understand and follow some multi-step directions for classroom related activities.

ELA Standard
Read narrative and expository text fluently and accurately with appropriate pacing, intonation, and expression.

13

Name   Date

b Word Families, Spelling Friends _y, _ies

▪ Review the meaning of each word on the following chart.

▪ Read the words in the box.

▪ Complete the chart.

Word	Definition	Sentence
dizzy		
fuzzy		
greedy		
ladies		
studies		
buddies		

14

Name _____   Date _____

ⓐ Demonstrating Comprehension

A class schedule tells us what happens everyday in the classroom. This is *my* class schedule.

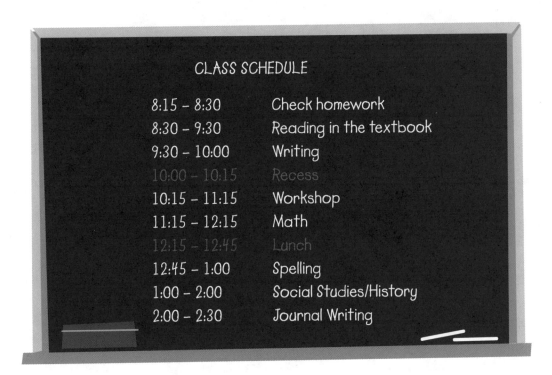

CLASS SCHEDULE

8:15 – 8:30	Check homework
8:30 – 9:30	Reading in the textbook
9:30 – 10:00	Writing
10:00 – 10:15	Recess
10:15 – 11:15	Workshop
11:15 – 12:15	Math
12:15 – 12:45	Lunch
12:45 – 1:00	Spelling
1:00 – 2:00	Social Studies/History
2:00 – 2:30	Journal Writing

1. What happens in the classroom at 12:45?
   - ☐ The students go to recess.
   - ☐ The students check their homework.
   - ☐ The students learn spelling words.
   - ☐ The students write in their journals.

2. If you go home at 2:00, you will miss —
   - ☐ math
   - ☐ social studies
   - ☐ reading
   - ☐ journal writing

3. What time does the class have workshop?
   - ☐ 8:15
   - ☐ 9:30
   - ☐ 10:15
   - ☐ 2:00

4. The first thing that happens in the day is —
   - ☐ check homework
   - ☐ reading in the workbook
   - ☐ workshop
   - ☐ journal writing

ELD Standard
   Retell simple stories using drawings, words, or phrases. Read simple vocabulary, phrases, and sentences independently.
ELA Standard
   Understand how text features make information accessible and usable.

Name _____ Date _____

b Writing Sentences

- Write and illustrate rules for your class.

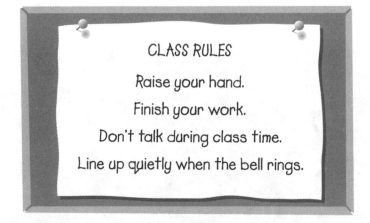

MY CLASS RULES

1 _____

_____

2 _____

_____

3 _____

_____

4 _____

_____

ELD Standard
Create simple sentences or phrases with some assistance.
ELA Standard
Use correct capitalization.

Name   Date

a Asking and Answering Questions

- Read the first sentence to your partner.
- Then ask your partner the question.
- Have your partner answer the question.

My Classroom

1  I have a notebook in my classroom.
Do you have a notebook in your classroom?

5  I have a chair in my classroom.
Do you have a chair in your classroom?

2  I have a desk in my classroom.
Do you have a desk in your classroom?

6  I have a computer in my classroom.
Do you have a computer in your classroom?

3 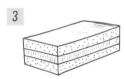 I have an eraser in my classroom.
Do you have an eraser in your classroom?

7  I have a chalkboard in my classroom.
Do you have a chalkboard in your classroom?

4  I have a stapler in my classroom.
Do you have a stapler in your classroom?

8  I have a bookcase in my classroom.
Do you have a bookcase in your classroom?

- Write two sentences about your classroom. Read the sentences to a partner.

_____

_____

_____

ELD Standard
   Ask and answer questions using phrases or simple sentences. Create simple sentences or phrases with some assistance.
ELA Standard
   Ask questions that seek information not already discussed.

Name _____   Date _____

b Writing Sentences

▪ Fill in the correct word in each sentence. Read the sentences to a partner.

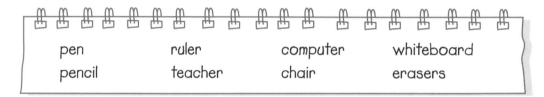

pen	ruler	computer	whiteboard
pencil	teacher	chair	erasers

1. I sit on a _____.

2. I play word games on the _____.

3. This _____ has red ink.

4. The teacher writes on the _____.

5. Mrs. Jones is my _____.

6. Can you find out how long the paper is by using the _____?

7. All the pencils have _____.

8. Please sharpen the _____.

▪ Write a sentence for each of the following words:

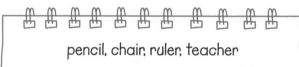

pencil, chair, ruler, teacher

1. _____

2. _____

3. _____

4. _____

ELD Standard
   Ask and answer questions using phrases or simple sentences. Create simple sentences or phrases with some assistance.
ELA Standard
   Use correct capitalization.

Name _____   Date _____

a Asking Questions Using *How Much*

■ Ask and answer the questions with a partner, using *how much*.

How much does the _____ cost?

SCHOOL STORE

box of pencils $5.25   dictionary $10.79   big eraser $2.30

backpack $20.95   school sweatshirt $10.99   notebook $6.79

1. How much does the dictionary cost?

   The dictionary costs _____.

2. How much does the school sweatshirt cost?

   The school sweatshirt costs _____.

3. How much does the dictionary and big eraser cost all together?

   The dictionary and big eraser cost _____.

4. How much does the box of pencils and big eraser cost all together?

   The box of pencils and big eraser cost _____.

ELD Standard
Ask and answer questions using phrases or simple sentences. Apply knowledge of content-related vocabulary to discussions and reading.
ELA Standard
Understand how text features (e.g., format, graphics, sequence, diagrams, illustrations, maps) make information accessible and usable.

▪ Write the questions.

5. The backpack costs $20.95.

   _____

6. The school sweatshirt costs $10.99.

   _____

▪ Answer the following questions.

7. You can get three things from the School Store. What do you want to buy?

   _____

   _____

   _____

   How much do these three things cost all together? _____

Name _____   Date _____

a Identifying Cause and Effect

- Look at the two pictures below:

✔ A <u>cause</u> is what makes something happen.

- **What is the cause in the picture?** Write your answer on the line.

_____

✔ An <u>effect</u> is what happens as the result of the cause.

- **What is the effect in the picture?**

_____

Cause   Effect

- Look at the pictures. Write a sentence to describe the cause and effect.

1. _____

2. _____

Cause

Effect

3. _____

4. _____

Cause

Effect

5. _____

6. _____

ELD Standard
Identify some significant structural (organizational) patterns in text, such as sequence/chronological order and cause/effect.
ELA Standard
Understand how text features (e.g., format, graphics, sequence, diagrams, illustrations, maps) make information accessible and usable.

Name _____　　　Date _____

b Word Families, Spelling Friends _ike, _ide

■ Review the meaning of each word on the following chart.

	Word	Definition	Sentence
1	like		
2	spike		
3	alike		
4	ride		
5	hide		
6	stride		

ELD Standard
Recognize English phonemes that correspond to phonemes students already hear and produce while reading aloud.
Begin to speak with a few words or sentences, using some English phonemes and rudimentary English grammatical forms.
ELA Standard
Spell roots, suffixes, prefixes, contractions, and syllable constructions correctly.

Name _____   Date _____

ⓐ Capitals and End Punctuation

▬ ▬ ▬ ▬ ▬ ▬ ▬ ▬ ▬ ▬ ▬ ▬ ▬ ▬ ▬ ▬ ▬ ▬

Capitals

✔ Use a capital letter for the following:
- The beginning of a sentence.   This is my family.
- The first letter of the names of cities,
  states, nations, and continents   I live in Dallas, Texas. Canada is not in Europe.
- The first letter of days of the week.   I go to school on Monday.

Punctuation

✔ Use a period at the end of a statement.   I live in Utah.
✔ Use a question mark at the end of a question.   Do you live in Alabama?

▬ ▬ ▬ ▬ ▬ ▬ ▬ ▬ ▬ ▬ ▬ ▬ ▬ ▬ ▬ ▬ ▬ ▬

- Rewrite the sentences. Put in capital letters and end punctuation.
- Read the sentences to a partner.

1. is the city of portland in the state of oregon or in the state of maine

   _____

2. pao goes to the movies on saturday

   _____

3. my father doesn't work on sunday

   _____

4. is your mother from russia or from finland

   _____

5. nicaragua, costa rica, panama, el salvador, honduras, guatemala, and belize are in central america

   _____

   _____

ELD Standard
   Use capital letters when writing names of cities and states. Use a period at the end of a sentence.
ELA Standard
   Use correct capitalization.

Name _____   Date _____

a Identifying Nouns

■ Underline and write the two nouns in each sentence.

Example: The <u>people</u> live in the <u>city</u>.

1. The teacher is in the classroom.   _____ _____

2. The students sit on the chairs.   _____ _____

3. The janitor keeps the cafeteria clean.   _____ _____

4. We play on the playground.   _____ _____

5. The principal is in the office.   _____ _____

6. The librarian is in the library.   _____ _____

7. The book is in my backpack.   _____ _____

8. Put your pencil in the desk.   _____ _____

9. The secretary works at the school.   _____ _____

10. The computer is in our classroom.   _____ _____

■ Write nouns that fit into each group.

people	places	things
11. _____	_____	_____
12. _____	_____	_____
13. _____	_____	_____

ELD Standard
    Use correct parts of speech.
ELA Standard
    Identify and correctly use verbs, modifiers, nouns, and pronouns.

Name _____   Date _____

b Word Families, Spelling Friends _ile, _ine

- Review the meaning of each word in the chalkboard.
- Write the correct word in each sentence.
- Read the sentences to a partner.

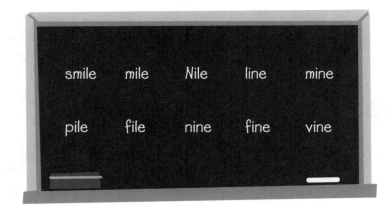

smile   mile   Nile   line   mine

pile   file   nine   fine   vine

1. The number _____ comes after eight and before ten.

2. The teacher drew a _____ in math class.

3. The _____ River is in Africa.

4. I feel _____ today. How are you?

5. The librarian has a _____ of books.

6. My friend and I are tired. We ran a _____.

7. Pao and Maylee _____ when I take their picture.

8. That CD is yours. This one is _____.

9. The farm worker picks grapes off a long _____.

10. At school the secretary has a _____ for each student.

ELD Standard
Recognize English phonemes that correspond to phonemes students already hear and produce while reading aloud.
Begin to speak with a few words or sentences, using some English phonemes and rudimentary English grammatical forms.

ELA Standard
Spell roots, suffixes, prefixes, contractions, and syllabic constructions correctly.

Name _____   Date _____

a Identifying Nouns

■ Complete the word maps with nouns that belong in each room.
   Read the words to a partner. Discuss the words. Discuss why the words are nouns.

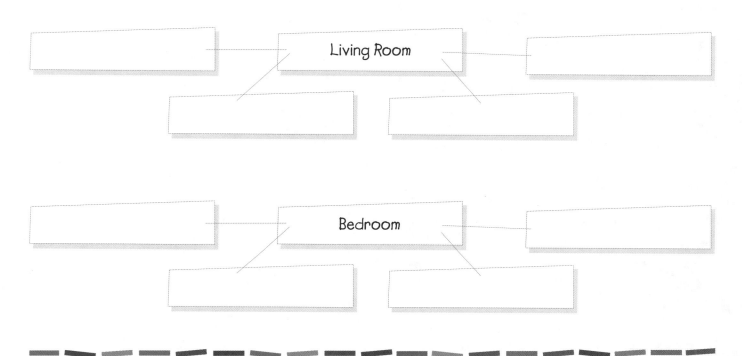

■ Write the words that belong in each room under the correct column.

Kitchen   Bathroom

bathtub
stove
shampoo
refrigerator
toothbrush
pots and pans
dishes

_____   _____

_____   _____

_____   _____

ELD Standard
   Use correct parts of speech. Ask and answer questions using phrases or simple sentences. Write an increasing number
   of words and simple sentences appropriate for language arts and other content areas.
ELA Standard
   Identify and correctly use verbs, modifiers, nouns, and pronouns.

27

Name _____   Date _____

b Word Families, Spelling Friends _ime, _ice, _ite, _ipe

- Complete the chart, using nouns.

	Word	Picture	Sentence
1	lime		
2	time		
3	mice		
4	Ms. Rice		
5	slice		
6	White Mountains		
7	kite		
8	pipe		

ELD Standard
Recognize English phonemes that correspond to phonemes students already hear and produce while reading aloud.
ELA Standard
Spell roots, suffixes, prefixes, contractions, and syllabic constructions correctly.

Name _____   Date _____

a Demonstrating Comprehension

■ Read the invitation to a partner. Answer the questions.

Come to My Birthday Party

My name is Mike.
I am having a birthday party.
This is how you ride your bike to my house.

1. Ride down Main Street.
2. Turn right at the stop sign onto Elm Street.
3. Go three blocks.
4. Turn left on First Street
5. My house is on the corner.
   My address is 800 First Street.

1. At the stop sign —
   ☐ go straight
   ☐ turn around
   ☐ turn right
   ☐ turn left

2. Mike's house is —
   ☐ in the middle
   ☐ on the corner
   ☐ on the right
   ☐ on the left

3. Who is having the birthday party?
   ☐ Juan
   ☐ Linda
   ☐ Pat
   ☐ Mike

4. Mike lives on —
   ☐ Main Street
   ☐ Elm Street
   ☐ Second Street
   ☐ First Street

5. This passage was written to —
   ☐ give directions to Mike's house
   ☐ give Mike's phone number
   ☐ tell what Mike's present are
   ☐ give a recipe for a birthday cake

6. What can you ride to Mike's house?
   ☐ a chair
   ☐ a lion
   ☐ a bike
   ☐ a box

ELD Standard
Identify the main idea in a story read aloud using key words and/or phrases.
ELA Standard
Discern main ideas and concepts presented in texts, identifying and assessing evidence that supports those ideas.

Name _____   Date _____

b Expository Writing

Writing Prompt

■ Write the directions to your house from the school.

Before Writing: Think about how you get to your house from the school.

After Writing: Read your directions to a partner. Draw a picture of your house.

Directions to My House from the School

1. _____

2. _____

3. _____

4. _____

5. _____

My address is _____

This is my house.

Name _____   Date _____

Identifying Singular Nouns and Plural Nouns

■ Write the plural form of the following nouns that are places in the community environment. Read the plural nouns to a partner.

1. park _____   6. apartment _____

2. school _____   7. movie theater _____

3. restaurant _____   8. supermarket _____

4. hospital _____   9. gas station _____

5. house _____   10. office _____

■ Write the correct plural form of the noun in each sentence. Read the sentences to a partner.

1. We eat dinner at our community's _____.

2. We play ball at our community's _____.

3. Children learn to read at our community's _____.

4. My mom and dad buy food at our community's _____.

5. We fill up the car's gas tank at our community's _____.

6. We check to see what's playing at the various _____.

7. Mike and Juan both live in _____.

8. Some people live on the eighth floor in _____.

ELD Standard
    Use correct parts of speech.
ELA Standard
    Identify and correctly use verbs, modifiers, nouns, and pronouns.

31

Name _____   Date _____

b Word Families, Spelling Friend _ight

- Read the poem to a partner. Underline all the words that end in _ight_.
- Read the words to a partner.

Turn on the Light

Turn on the light.
Turn on the light.
Mom's working tonight.
Mom's working on a flight.
She's helping passengers who are uptight.
Turn on the light.
Mom's working tonight.
She's waiting on tables and cleaning off tables just right.
Turn on the light.
Mom's working tonight.
She's a police officer who's breaking up fights.
Turn on the light.
Mom's working tonight.
She's a detective staying out of sight.
Turn on the light.
Mom's working tonight.
Mom is very bright.
She might be working on a flight.
She might be cleaning the tables off just right.
She might be breaking up fights.
She might be a detective staying out of sight.
Turn on the light.
Mom's working tonight.

ELD Standard
   Generate the sounds from all the letters and letter patterns, including phonograms, and blend these sounds into recognizable words. Identify the main idea in a story that is read aloud, using key words or phrases.
ELA Standard
   Spell roots, suffixes, prefixes, contractions, and syllabic constructions correctly. Read aloud narrative and expository text fluently, accurately, and with appropriate pacing, intonation, and expression.

1. What is this poem mainly about?
   - [ ] Mom's jobs
   - [ ] Dad's jobs
   - [ ] a flight
   - [ ] a light .

2. What is Mom doing on the flight?
   - [ ] turning off the light
   - [ ] helping passengers who are uptight
   - [ ] waiting on tables
   - [ ] staying out of sight

3. What does Mom do when she's a detective?
   - [ ] breaks up fights
   - [ ] sleeps
   - [ ] stays out of sight
   - [ ] cleans off tables

4. Light rhymes with —
   - [ ] turn
   - [ ] Mom
   - [ ] right
   - [ ] out

5. Mom has many —
   - [ ] lamps
   - [ ] friends
   - [ ] hats
   - [ ] jobs

6. What are Mom's professions?
   - [ ] flight attendant, firefighter, police officer, supermarket cashier
   - [ ] gas station attendant, firefighter, postal worker, park ranger
   - [ ] flight attendant, waitress, police officer, detective
   - [ ] flight attendant, waitress, postal worker, doctor

■ Draw a picture of someone doing one of the jobs.

■ In the notepad, write a sentence about that person's job.

Name _____   Date _____

a Demonstrating Listening Comprehension

▬ ▬ ▬ ▬ ▬ ▬ ▬ ▬ ▬ ▬ ▬ ▬ ▬ ▬ ▬ ▬ ▬ ▬ ▬

- ■ Read the questions. Then read the story to a partner.
- ■ Answer the questions.

My Grandmother

My name is Sam. I was born in America. My grandmother's name is Mrs. Nguyen. She was born in Vietnam. I like hamburgers. My grandmother likes pho bo, a beef and rice noodle soup. I play rock and roll. My grandmother plays the zither. I like to read storybooks. My grandmother likes to read letters from my uncle in Vietnam. I like to draw. My grandmother does too. My grandmother makes a point on her brush. I make a point on my brush, too. My grandmother draws a fish. I draw a fish, too. My grandmother teaches me her art. It brings us joy.

1. What is this story mainly about?
   - ☐ a family named Nguyen
   - ☐ a place in Vietnam
   - ☐ things the grandmother and grandchild enjoy doing

2. What is pho bo?
   - ☐ a type of cake
   - ☐ a grandchild
   - ☐ a beef and rice noodle soup

3. Where was Sam born?
   - ☐ Vietnam
   - ☐ United States
   - ☐ Mexico

4. Where is the grandmother from?
   - ☐ America
   - ☐ Mexico
   - ☐ Vietnam

5. What is a zither?
   - ☐ a toy
   - ☐ a musical instrument
   - ☐ a couch

6. Which sentence pair shows that Sam and his grandmother have something in common?
   - ☐ I play rock and roll. My grandmother plays the zither.
   - ☐ I like to read storybooks. My grandmother likes to read letters from my uncle in Vietnam.
   - ☐ I like to draw. My grandmother does too.

ELD Standard
Identify the main idea in a story read aloud using key words and/or phrases.
ELA Standard
Discern main ideas and concepts presented in texts, identifying and assessing evidence that supports those ideas.

Name _____   Date _____

b Descriptive Writing

Writing Prompt

Before Writing: Make a word map, using words to describe your grandmother.

My Grandmother

- Draw a picture and describe your grandmother.
- Write a description of your grandmother.

My Grandmother is _____

_____

_____

_____

_____

After Writing: Read your description to a partner.

ELD Standard
Use capital letters at the beginning of sentences. Use a period at the end of a sentence. Use complete sentences and correct word order. Begin to use a variety of genres in writing.
ELA Standards
Write narrative, expository, persuasive, and descriptive texts.

35

Name _____   Date _____

a Demonstrating Comprehension

Multicultural Community Event

Multicultural Art Auction

Bring your multicultural sculptures, paintings, drawings, etc. for an auction.

Sunday, July 16

2:00 P.M. to 4:00 P.M.

Lincoln Park

Call Maria Castro for information: 627-5523

Multicultural Music and Dancing

Friday, July 14

5:00 P.M. to 7:00 P.M.

Lincoln Park Community Center

Adults $3.00

Children $1.00

Multicultural Book Fair

Thursday, July 13

10:00 A.M.

Lincoln Park Library

Sponsored by Jane Ward

Multicultural Food Tasting

Saturday, July 15

11:00 A.M.

Lincoln Park Community Center

Entry Fee: $5.00

Call Mark Ramirez for information: 627-1273

1. On which day can you attend the Multicultural Art Auction?
   - [ ] Sunday
   - [ ] Wednesday
   - [ ] Saturday
   - [ ] Friday

2. Who can you call if you want more information about the Multicultural Book Fair?
   - [ ] Maria Castro
   - [ ] Mark Ramirez
   - [ ] Jane Ward
   - [ ] Mike James

3. Which event is not part of the Multicultural Community Events?
   - [ ] Multicultural Videos
   - [ ] Multicultural Food Tasting
   - [ ] Multicultural Music and Dancing
   - [ ] Multicultural Art Auction

4. What would you most likely do at an auction?
   - [ ] eat dinner
   - [ ] watch a movie
   - [ ] buy something
   - [ ] mow the lawn

ELD Standard
Identify the main idea in a story that is read aloud, using key words or phrases.
ELA Standard
Discern main ideas and concepts presented in texts, identifying and assessing evidence that supports those ideas.

Name _____   Date _____

ⓑ Descriptive Writing

▬ ▬ ▬ ▬ ▬ ▬ ▬ ▬ ▬ ▬ ▬ ▬ ▬ ▬ ▬ ▬ ▬ ▬ ▬ ▬

Writing Prompt

Before Writing: Make a word map, using words to describe your favorite multicultural food.

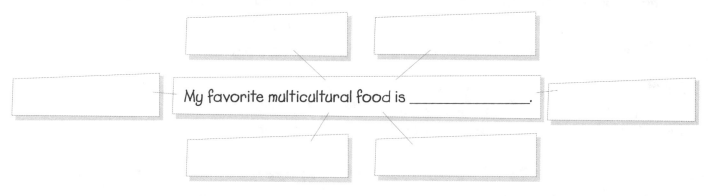

My favorite multicultural food is _____.

■ Draw a picture of the multicultural food that you like best.
Describe what the food looks like, how the food tastes and what the food smells like.

This is a picture of my favorite food.

It is _____.

This multicultural food looks _____.

This multicultural food tastes _____.

This multicultural food smells _____.

This multicultural food is the best because

_____.

I like this multicultural food because

_____.

You make this multicultural food with

_____.

I eat this multicultural food with

_____.

After Writing: Read your description to a partner.

ELD Standard
   Use capital letters when writing the word *I* and at the beginning of a sentence. Use a period at the end of a sentence.
ELA Standard
   Write narrative, expository, persuasive, and descriptive texts.

Name   Date

a Capitals and End Punctuation

Capitals

✔ Use a capital letter for the following:

■ The beginning of a sentence.   There is a beach in our community.

■ The word *I*.   I am eleven years old.

■ The first letter of people's names.   Lupita is a girl.

Punctuation

✔ Use a period at the end of a statement.   He is a boy.

✔ Use a question mark at the end of a question.   Is she happy?

■ Review capitals and end punctuation on page 24.

■ Rewrite the sentences. Put in capital letters and end punctuation.

■ Read the sentences to a partner.

1. i think our community is one of the best in the united states

    _____

2. did you see miguel play soccer at the community park

    _____

3. carlos and his dad go to the saturday farmers' market

    _____

4. antonio catches catfish in the community river park

    _____

5. where do you go to the movies in our community

    _____

Name _____   Date _____

b Word Families, Spelling Friends _ose, _one

- Read the words in the box.
- Write the correct word in each sentence.
- Put the correct punctuation at the end of every sentence.
- Read the sentences to a partner.

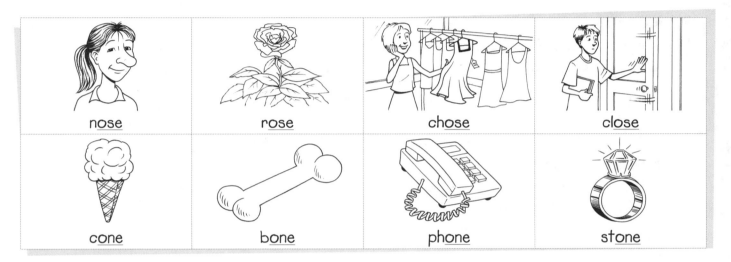

| nose | rose | chose | close |
| cone | bone | phone | stone |

Example: Is this *your dog's bone?*

1. There is a beautiful _____ bush in the garden

2. Please _____ the door

3. Please give me the ice cream _____

4. Where is the dress you _____ at the store

5. He is always talking on the _____

6. Please put the blue _____ in the ring

7. Margarita has a very large _____

8. Is this the big dog's _____

ELD Standard
   Recognize English phonemes that correspond to phonemes students already hear and produce while reading aloud.
ELA Standard
   Spell roots, suffixes, prefixes, contractions, and syllabic constructions correctly.

Name _____   Date _____

a Capitals and End Punctuation

Capitals
✔ Begin the first word of a sentence with capital letter. *This is my state.*
✔ Always use a capital letter for the word *I*. *I live in California.*
✔ Always use a capital letter for the first letter of the names of cities, states and nations.
  I live in Sacramento, California. I live in the United States.

Punctuation
✔ Use a period at the end of a statement. *I live in Utah.*
✔ Use a question mark at the end of a question. *Do you live in Texas?*

- Rewrite the sentences. Put in capitals and ending punctuation.
- Read the sentences to a partner.

1. alaska, texas and california are very big states

_____

2. do i fly north or south from alabama to get to vermont

_____

3. atlanta is the capital of georgia and boston is the capital of massachusetts

_____

4. the colors of the united states' flag are red, white and blue

_____

5. i am going to visit my grandma in miami, florida

_____

6. my mother is from canada and my father is from mexico

_____

ELD Standard
   Use capital letters when writing names of cities, states, and countries. Use a period at the end of a sentence.
ELA Standard
   Use correct capitalization.

Name _____   Date _____

b Word Families, Spelling Friends _ome, _ole, _ope, _oke

■ Complete the chart.

Word	Picture	Sentence
1 d<u>ome</u>		
2 h<u>ome</u>		
3 m<u>ole</u>		
4 p<u>ole</u>		
5 r<u>ope</u>		
6 sl<u>ope</u>		
7 sm<u>oke</u>		
8 p<u>oke</u>		

ELD Standard
   Recognize English phonemes that correspond to phonemes students already hear and produce while reading aloud.
ELA Standard
   Spell roots, suffixes, prefixes, contractions, and syllabic constructions correctly.

Name _____   Date _____

ⓐ Common and Proper Nouns

■ Read the words on the chalkboard with a partner.
Write the correct proper noun next to the common noun.

United States   Texas
Chavez School   Fifth Street
Los Angeles   Southeast Region
Pacific Ocean   Hudson River
Miss Gomez   *Treasure Island*
Miguel   White House

1. boy _____

2. school _____

3. state _____

4. ocean _____

5. region _____

6. city _____

7. street _____

8. building _____

9. teacher _____

10. book _____

11. country _____

12. river _____

ELD Standard
Use capital letters to begin sentences and proper nouns.
ELA Standard
Use correct capitalization. Identify and correctly use verbs, modifiers, nouns, and pronouns.

Name _____   Date _____

b Word Families, Spelling Friends _oat, _ow

■ Read the poem to a partner. Switch roles. Underline the words with _oat.

■ Read the words to a partner.

The Goat's Boat

Look at the goat.
There's a big bow at his throat.

Look at the goat.
He's wearing a gold coat.

Look at the goat.
He wants to sail the boat.

Look at the goat.
Can the goat make the boat float?

Look at the goat.
The goat pushes the boat.

The boat is too slow.
Look at the goat.

The goat doesn't know how
to make the boat go.

1. Who is sailing the boat?
   - ☐ the cat
   - ☐ the goat
   - ☐ the boy
   - ☐ the girl

2. Which of these pairs of words from the poem rhyme?
   - ☐ look, coat
   - ☐ goat, slow
   - ☐ throat, float
   - ☐ how, go

3. Which of these lines from the poem have words that begin with the same sound?
   - ☐ He's wearing a gold coat.
   - ☐ Look at the goat.
   - ☐ He wants to sail the boat.
   - ☐ There's a big bow at his throat.

4. What is this poem mainly about?
   - ☐ a goat with a boat
   - ☐ a big bow
   - ☐ a gold coat
   - ☐ a big cat

5. Which of these lines sounds like it could be part of the poem?
   - ☐ Where is the ship?
   - ☐ The goat sails the boat in the moat.
   - ☐ Is the goat going on a plane?
   - ☐ The dog likes to fly his kite.

6. Which word rhymes with "know"?
   - ☐ look
   - ☐ cat
   - ☐ goat
   - ☐ show

■ Create a series of rhyming words. Begin the series with the word *goat*.

goat ⟶ moat ⟶

■ What is your favorite line from the poem? Draw a picture.

Name _____ Date _____

a Plural Nouns

✔ To change singular to plural nouns, add *s*.

nation ⟶ *nation<u>s</u>*

✔ To form the plural of most nouns ending in *s*, *x*, *ch*, *sh*, or *z*, add *es*.

rich ⟶ *rich<u>es</u>*

✔ To form the plural of a few nouns, change the word completely.

person ⟶ <u>*people*</u>

A nation is a people united under one government. Our nation is the United States of America. Our nation has many riches, such as its natural resources and people. Our nation is a melting pot because people with different cultures, languages and customs live and work here. Our nation has immigrants from all over the world. They come to our country on planes, trains, buses, even on foot. They come to our nation to complete their wishes to work hard and have a good future. They pay taxes and help build a great nation.

■ Read the passage to a partner. Underline the plural nouns.

■ Write the plural forms of the nouns below.

1. watch _____

2. border _____

3. fax _____

4. address _____

5. box _____

6. dish _____

7. fizz _____

8. gas _____

9. person _____

10. lime _____

ELD Standard
Spell correctly one-syllable words, changing the ending of a word when forming a plural.
ELA Standard
Identify and correctly use verbs that are often misused, modifiers, nouns, and pronouns.

Name _____ Date _____

b Word Families, Spelling Friends _use, _ew

- Complete the chart.
- Read the sentences to a partner.

Word	Noun or Verb	Sentence
<u>use</u>		
f<u>use</u>		
am<u>use</u>		
acc<u>use</u>		
ab<u>use</u>		
ref<u>use</u>		
m<u>ew</u>		
ch<u>ew</u>		

ELD Standard
   Recognize English phonemes that correspond to phonemes students already hear and produce while reading aloud.
   Use correct parts of speech.
ELA Standard
   Spell roots, suffixes, prefixes, contractions, and syllabic constructions correctly.

Name _____   Date _____

a Forming Plural Nouns with _ies and _eys

✔ To form the plural of a singular noun that ends with a consonant and *y*, change the *y* to *i* and add *es*.

The <u>nursery</u> has pots made in a <u>factory</u>. ⟶ *The <u>nurseries</u> have pots made in <u>factories</u>.*

✔ To form the plural of a singular noun that ends with *ey*, add *s*.

The <u>key</u> opens the door. ⟶ *The <u>keys</u> open the door.*

A Factory

A <u>factory</u> is a building where products are manufactured. Many different kinds of products are manufactured in <u>factories</u>. People in <u>factories</u> produce toys, cars, food, computers, clothes and airplanes. <u>Factories</u> also produce car seats for <u>babies</u>, flowerpots for <u>nurseries</u>, books that tell <u>stories</u>, and <u>keys</u> to open doors. All of these items can be made cheaper and faster in a factory than if they were handmade by just one person.

■ Write the plural form of each singular noun.
■ Write a sentence for each plural noun.
■ Read your sentences to a partner.

1. factory _____ _____

2. baby _____ _____

3. alley _____ _____

4. story _____ _____

5. nursery _____ _____

6. body _____ _____

7. industry _____ _____

8. valley _____ _____

ELD Standard
Spell correctly one-syllable words, changing the ending of a word.
ELA Standard
Identify and correctly use verbs that are often misused, modifiers, nouns, and pronouns.

Name _____ Date _____

b Word Families, Spelling Friends _at, _an, _ack

- Read the words in the box. Use each word in a sentence.
- Read your sentences to a partner.

| 1 cat | 2 mat | 3 pat | 4 man | 5 pan |

| 6 van | 7 pack | 8 tack | 9 stack |

1. _____

2. _____

3. _____

4. _____

5. _____

6. _____

7. _____

8. _____

9. _____

ELD Standard
Recognize English phonemes that correspond to phonemes students already hear and produce while reading aloud.
Use correct parts of speech.
ELA Standard
Spell roots, suffixes, prefixes, contractions, and syllabic constructions correctly.

Name   Date

a Forming Plural Nouns with *os* and *oes*

✔ To form the plural of a singular noun that ends with a vowel and *o*, add *s*.

radio ⟶ radios

✔ To form the plural of a singular noun that ends with a consonant and *o*, add *s* or *es*.

silo ⟶ silos
hero ⟶ heroes

✔ Since the nouns ending in *o* can take one of two endings, be sure to check your dictionary if you are unsure whether the noun ending in an *o* takes an <u>s</u> or an <u>es</u> for its plural.

Singular Noun	Plural Nouns
potato	potatoes
rodeo	rodeos
hero	heroes
pinto	pintos
radio	radios
tomato	tomatoes
video	videos
silo	silos
photo	photos

ELD Standard
Spell correctly one-syllable words, changing the ending of a word.
ELA Standard
Identify and correctly use verbs that are often misused, modifiers, nouns, and pronouns.

49

- Fill in the blank in each sentence with the correct plural noun from the box.

- Read the sentences to a partner.

- Draw a picture of one of the sentences.

1. Farms have barns and _____ to store grain.

2. _____ have calf roping competitions and stunt riding.

3. The farm has ten cows and twelve _____.

4. The moviemakers took _____ of the farmers on their tractors.

5. The farmers grow _____ along with other vegetables.

6. The _____ are broadcasting the weather report for the farmers.

7. The farmers' _____ grow under the ground.

8. The farmers are _____ because they help supply food for the people of the United States.

9. The reporters are going to print the _____ of farm life in the newspaper.

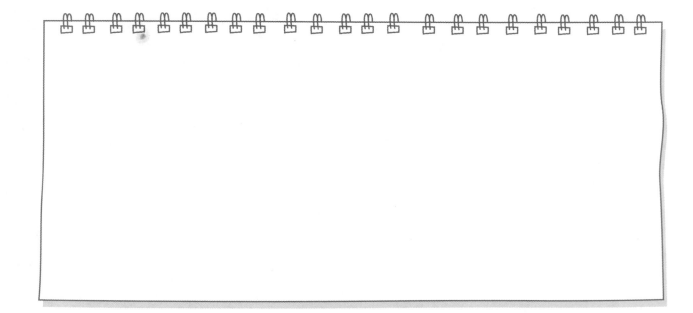

Name _____   Date _____

a Demonstrating Listening Comprehension

- Read each story to a partner. Your partner *sums up* the main idea. Switch roles.
- Fill in the bubble for the sentence that tells the main idea.
- Write a sentence to tell what the story is mainly about.

The <u>main idea</u> of a story tells what the story is about.

People Have Different Jobs

People in a community have different jobs. They depend upon each other for goods and services. Some people in the community provide goods and services to other community members when they do their jobs.

Some people produce goods or products through their jobs. Factory workers make cars, computers, televisions and other products. People in the community use these products.

This story is mainly about —
- ☐ factory workers who make cars
- ☐ people in the community who use products
- ☐ people in the community who have different jobs

- Write a sentence that tells what this story is mainly about.

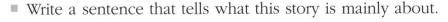

ELD Standard
   Identify the main idea in a story that is read aloud using key words or phrases.
ELA Standard
   Discern main ideas and concepts presented in texts, identifying and assessing evidence that supports those ideas.

Farmers

Farmers produce food for the community. Some farmers grow different kinds of vegetables on their farms. This type of farming is called diversified farming. Diversified farming means that many crops are grown together on a farm. For example, corn, tomatoes, squash and beans might all be grown on the same farm.

This story is mainly about —
- [ ] the farmer who grows only corn on his farm
- [ ] farmers who use diversified farming to grow many crops
- [ ] beans and corn that grow separately on two different farms

■ Write a sentence that tells what this story is mainly about.

Service Jobs

Some people in the community have service jobs. People who have service jobs do not manufacture a product. Instead, they do something to help people in the community. Police officers have service jobs. They work to keep the community safe. Bus drivers are also service workers. They drive the buses and provide transportation for people in the community. There are many other service workers in the community including doctors, nurses, teachers and firefighters.

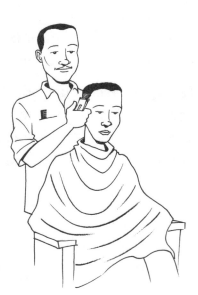

This story is mainly about —
- [ ] firefighters who put out fires
- [ ] some people in the community who have service jobs
- [ ] people who drive buses

■ Write a sentence that tells what this story is mainly about.

Name _____   Date _____

a Identifying the Main Idea

- Read each passage. Answer the questions.
- Underline all the plural nouns in the passages.
- Read the passage to a partner. Your partner *sums up* what you have read. Switch roles.

Construction Workers Build Industrial Buildings

Construction workers build different kinds of buildings on different types of land. They build factories, warehouses and other industrial buildings on industrial land. These factories manufacture products for people in the community.

This passage is mainly about —
- ☐ industrial buildings that are large
- ☐ construction workers who build industrial buildings on industrial land
- ☐ a factory that produces products

Construction Workers Build Recreational Parks

Construction workers build recreational parks on recreational land. They build the buildings and structures for the rides at amusement parks. They build these recreational buildings so people can go to the parks to have a good time.

This passage is mainly about —
- ☐ construction workers who build recreational buildings
- ☐ amusement parks around the United States
- ☐ people who have fun at amusement parks

Construction Workers Build Agricultural Buildings

Construction workers build agricultural buildings on agricultural land. They build silos and barns on agricultural land. Farmers store grain in the silos. They keep their cows in the barns.

This passage is mainly about —
- ☐ cows that stay in the barns
- ☐ construction workers who build agricultural buildings on agricultural land
- ☐ farmers who store grain in silos

ELD Standard
    Identify the main idea in a story that is read aloud using key words or phrases.
ELA Standard
    Discern main ideas and concepts presented in texts, identifying and assessing evidence that supports those ideas.

Name   Date

b Categorizing, Spelling Friend _ial

▪ Write the words that belong with each type of land usage.

▪ On a separate sheet of paper, make mind maps of recreational land and agricultural land.

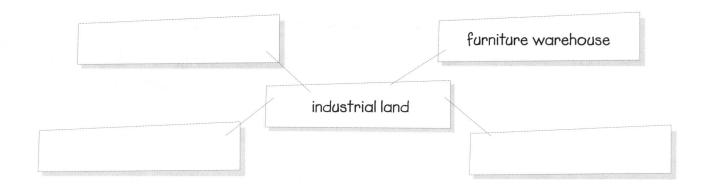

car factory	furniture factory	orchard	car repair shop
amusement park	barbershop	almond farm	lumber warehouse
truck farm	restaurant	computer factory	movie theater
supermarket	airport	vineyard	paper warehouses
walnut grove	miniature golf course	fairgrounds	city park

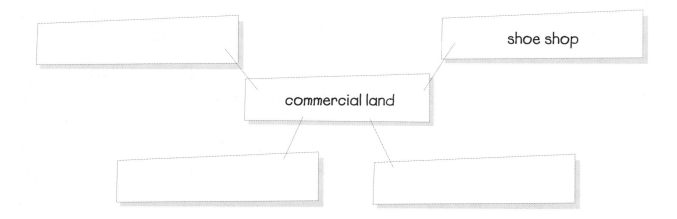

ELD Standard
    Apply knowledge of content-related vocabulary to discussions and readings.
ELA Standard
    Spell roots, suffixes, prefixes, contractions, and syllabic constructions correctly.

Name _____   Date _____

ⓐ Capitals: Titles of People

━ ━ ━ ━ ━ ━ ━ ━ ━ ━ ━ ━ ━ ━ ━ ━ ━ ━ ━ ━

✔ Begin a sentence with a capital letter. *This is her bus.*

✔ Always use a capital letter when you write the word *I*. *I live in the community.*

✔ Begin the names and titles of people with a capital letter. *This is Dr. F. Jones. This is Uncle Carlos.*

✔ Use capital letters when you write initials. *This is Mrs. C. E. Warren.*

━ ━ ━ ━ ━ ━ ━ ━ ━ ━ ━ ━ ━ ━ ━ ━ ━ ━ ━ ━

■ Write each sentence over correctly. Read the sentences to a partner.

1. this is the hospital where dr. e. jones is an employee. _____

   _____

2. is mrs. f. ramirez a service worker in a local business? _____

   _____

3. i think mrs. f. reyes is a manager in a factory. _____

   _____

4. are you going to visit uncle carlos? _____

5. this lady works as a nurse. her name is miss w. adams. _____

   _____

6. did you know that aunt linda opened her own company? _____

   _____

7. what kind of career does mr. l. ellis have? _____

8. this is the office of mr. e. w. clark. _____

ELD Standard
  Use capital letters to begin proper nouns.
ELA Standard
  Use correct capitalization.

55

Name _____   Date _____

b Word Families, Spelling Friends _and, _ask

- Read the words on the chalkboard.
- Write the correct word next to each picture.
- Write a sentence for each word.
- Read the sentences to a partner.

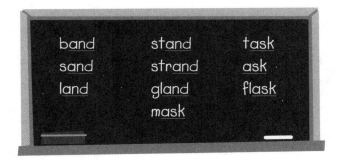

band	stand	task
sand	strand	ask
land	gland	flask
	mask	

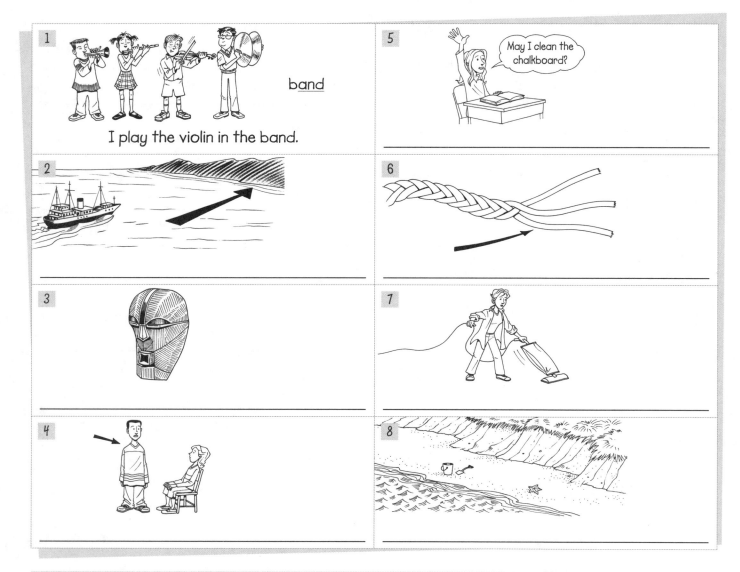

1
b<u>and</u>

I play the violin in the band.

5
May I clean the chalkboard?

2

6

3

7

4

8

ELD Standard
Recognize English phonemes that correspond to phonemes students already hear and produce while reading aloud.
ELA Standard
Spell roots, suffixes, prefixes, contractions, and syllabic constructions correctly.

Name _____   Date _____

c Simple and Complete Subjects

✔ The subject of a sentence tells us what or whom the sentence is about.

✔ A <u>simple subject</u> is a subject that contains one word.
<u>Nurses</u> help sick people.

✔ A <u>complete subject</u> is a subject that contains two or more words.
<u>Those caring nurses</u> help sick people.

■ Draw a line under the subject of each sentence.

1. Doctors treat people who are sick.

2. Nurse practitioners help doctors to care for patients.

3. Those brave paramedics take care of people on the way to the hospital.

4. An ambulance is a vehicle that takes sick people to the hospital.

5. A biologist studies plants and animals.

6. That young woman is learning to be a doctor.

7. Many people work in science and health care.

■ Write three sentences about health care. Underline the subject in each sentence.

■ Read the sentences to a partner.

1. _____

_____

2. _____

_____

3. _____

_____

ELD Standard
    Use correct parts of speech, including subject/verb agreement.
ELA Standard
    Identify and correctly use sentence structures.

Name _____   Date _____

a Action Verbs

✔ An <u>action verb</u> expresses action.

✔ Action verbs show what the subject does.

The firefighter <u>fights</u> fires.

The gardener <u>plants</u> flowers.

cleans	collects	teaches
programs	connects	repairs
fights	plants	serves

▪ Write the correct action verb in each sentence. Read the sentences to a partner.

1. The firefighter _____ fires in the community.

2. The mechanic _____ car engines.

3. The housekeeper _____ hotel rooms.

4. The electrician _____ electrical wires in our houses.

5. A teacher _____ children how to read.

6. A gardener _____ flowers in gardens.

7. A computer programmer _____ computers.

8. A trash collector _____ the garbage every week.

▪ Write a sentence for each of the following words: serves, plants, cleans, collects.

Example: **A waiter serves food in a restaurant.**

1. _____

2. _____

3. _____

4. _____

ELD Standard
   Use correct parts of speech, including subject/verb agreement.
ELA Standard
   Identify and correctly use sentence structures.

Name _____　　　　Date _____

b Word Families, Spelling Friends _ed, _en, _et, _ent

- Read the words on the chart.
- Complete the chart.
- Read the sentences to a partner.

Word	Noun or Verb	Sentence
b<u>ed</u>		
sl<u>ed</u>		
l<u>ed</u>		
h<u>en</u>		
p<u>en</u>		
g<u>et</u>		
p<u>et</u>		
t<u>ent</u>		
r<u>ent</u>		
w<u>ent</u>		
sp<u>ent</u>		

ELD Standard
　　Recognize English phonemes that correspond to phonemes students already hear and produce while reading aloud.
　　Use correct parts of speech.
ELA Standard
　　Spell roots, suffixes, prefixes, contractions, and syllabic constructions correctly.

Name _____   Date _____

ⓐ Present Tense Verbs

▬ ▬ ▬ ▬ ▬ ▬ ▬ ▬ ▬ ▬ ▬ ▬ ▬ ▬ ▬ ▬ ▬ ▬ ▬ ▬

Rules for Forming Present Tense Verbs

✔ For most verbs, add *s*.

run/runs, sit/sits, talk/talks

✔ For verbs ending in *s*, *ch*, *sh*, *x* or *z*, add *es*.

watch/watches, push/pushes, mix/mixes

✔ For verbs ending in a consonant and *y*, change *y* to *i* and add *es*.

try/tries, hurry/hurries

▬ ▬ ▬ ▬ ▬ ▬ ▬ ▬ ▬ ▬ ▬ ▬ ▬ ▬ ▬ ▬ ▬ ▬ ▬ ▬

■ Add the correct present tense ending to the main form of the verb in parenthesis at the end of each sentence.

■ Read the sentences to a partner.

1. Marcos _____ television for entertainment. (watch)

2. Jan _____ to the music at the concert. (listen)

3. Nicolas _____ with Maria at the party. (dance)

4. The actress _____ the part of Cinderella. (play)

5. The radio announcer _____ that there will be rain on Sunday. (say)

6. The instructor _____ her how to play the guitar. (teach)

7. The illustrator _____ the illustrations to the script. (attach)

8. Margarita _____ after dancing in the musical. (relax)

9. The television industry _____ people to be creative. (encourage)

10. The scriptwriter _____ in the movie industry. (work)

11. In the soap opera, the hero _____ a lot. (cry)

60

ELD Standard
   Use correct parts of speech, including subject/verb agreement.
ELA Standard
   Identify and correctly use verbs, modifiers, nouns, and pronouns.

Name _____   Date _____

ᵇ Word Families, Spelling Friends _ig, _ish

- Read the sentences on the notepad. Underline the short ĭ words.
- Write the correct sentence under each picture. Underline the short ĭ words.
- Read the sentences to a partner.

Dad puts the <u>dish</u> on the table.

The fig turns purple when it is ripe.

Mike is going to wish on the wishbone.

The pig has a wig.

The pig is going to dig up the pit.

The fish is going to swish up the stream.

1 _____

4 _____

2 _____

5 _____

3 _____

6 _____

ELD Standard
Recognize most common English word parts. Generate the sounds from all letters and letter patterns, including consonant blends and long- and short-vowel patterns (phonograms), and blend these sounds into recognizable words.
ELA Standard
Spell roots, suffixes, prefixes, contractions, and syllabic constructions correctly.

Name _____   Date _____

a Subject-Verb Agreement with Singular Subjects

Subject-Verb Agreement

✔ The verb must agree with the subject in number.

✔ A singular subject takes a singular verb.

✔ Add *s* or *es* to a present tense verb when the subject is singular.
(Add *es* to verbs ending in *ch*, *sh*, *x* or *z*.)

Mark runs the race.
(The subject <u>Mark</u> is singular, so you add *s* to the main form of the verb *run*.)

The girl watches television.
(The subject <u>*the girl*</u> is singular, so you add *es* to the main form of the verb *watch*. Add *es* because the verb ends in *ch*.)

■ Complete the sentences by putting in the correct present tense form of the verb in parentheses.

■ Read your sentences to a partner.

1. Maria _____ to be a doctor when she grows up. (plan)

2. Pao _____ the news. He wants to be a television news reporter. (watch)

3. Jose _____ his science homework. (finish)

4. Susan _____ her toes. She is practicing to be a dancer. (touch)

5. The football coach _____ the gate to the football field. (latch)

6. Carol _____ about becoming a dentist. (think)

7. Dan _____ the button in the elevator. (push)

8. The boy _____ the doorbell on the house. (buzz)

9. Paul _____ the ingredients to make a cake. (mix)

ELD Standard
Use correct parts of speech, including subject/verb agreement.
ELA Standard
Identify and correctly use verbs, modifiers, nouns, and pronouns.

Name _____   Date _____

b Word Families, Spelling Friends _ick, _ill, _ive

- Read the words and fill in the chart.
- Read the sentences to a partner.

Word	Noun or Verb	Picture	Sentence
k<u>ick</u>			
st<u>ick</u>			
J<u>ill</u>			
h<u>ill</u>			
p<u>ill</u>			
l<u>ive</u>			
g<u>ive</u>			

ELD Standard
    Recognize most common English word parts. Generate the sounds from all letter patterns, including consonant blends
    and long- and short-vowel patterns (phonograms), and blend these sounds into recognizable words.
ELA Standard
    Spell roots, suffixes, prefixes, contractions, and syllabic constructions correctly.

Name _____   Date _____

ⓐ Subject–Verb Agreement with Plural Subjects

✔ Verbs agree with their subjects in number.

✔ Do not add *s* or *es* to the present-tense verb when the subject is a plural noun, or *I*, *you*, *we*, or *they*.

The students <u>study</u> for the test. They <u>write</u> the sentences. The boys <u>talk</u> on the cell phone.

Rule   If the subject ends in *s*, the verb can't end in *s*.
If the subject doesn't end in *s*, the verb can end in *s*.

■ In each sentence, underline the verb that goes with the plural form of the subject.

■ Write each sentence over correctly. Read the sentences to a partner.

1. My brothers and I (help/helps) people rake their lawns.

_____

2. The volunteers (work/works) for the American Red Cross.

_____

3. They (play/plays) chess at the chess club.

_____

4. The student committees (establish/establishes) the playground rules.

_____

5. The children (contribute/contributes) money to charity.

_____

6. You (include/includes) all of the computer club members on the advertisement.

_____

ELD Standard
Use correct parts of speech, including subject/verb agreement.
ELA Standard
Identify and correctly use verbs, modifiers, nouns, and pronouns.

Name _____   Date _____

b Word Families, Spelling Friends _ox, _op, _ot

- Read the words in the box.
- Write the correct word in each sentence.
- Read the sentences to a partner.
- Write <u>noun</u> or <u>verb</u> next to the words.

1	2	3
f<u>ox</u>	b<u>ox</u>	h<u>op</u>
4	5	6
m<u>op</u>	t<u>op</u>	ch<u>op</u>
7	8	9
p<u>ot</u>	kn<u>ot</u>	sp<u>ot</u>

ELD Standard
    Recognize English phonemes that correspond to phonemes students already hear and produce while reading aloud.
ELA Standard
    Spell roots, suffixes, prefixes, contractions, and syllabic constructions correctly.

1. The man is cooking the soup in a _____.

2. The boy put the books in a _____.

3. I clean with a _____.

4. Please _____ the wood.

5. Put the _____ on the bottle.

6. The bunny can _____.

7. The _____ has a big red tail.

8. Marcos makes a _____ in the rope.

9. The dog has a _____ on his face.

NOUN or VERB

✔ A <u>noun</u> is the name of a person, place or thing. A <u>verb</u> is an action word.

■ Write <u>noun</u> or <u>verb</u> on the line to show how each word was used in the sentences above.

fox _____noun_____   mop _____   pot _____

box _____   top _____   knot _____

hop _____   chop _____   spot _____

Name _____   Date _____

a Adjectives That Compare

✔ An <u>adjective</u> is a word that describes a noun. *Asia is a <u>big</u> continent.*
The word <u>big</u> describes the continent of Asia.

✔ <u>Adjectives</u> can also be used to compare two nouns. *My house is <u>bigger</u> than your house.*

✔ <u>Adjectives</u> can be used to compare more than two nouns.
Russia is the <u>biggest</u> country in the world.

 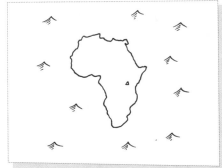 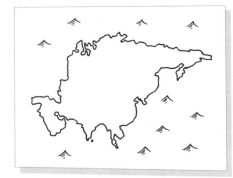

■ Underline the correct word in each sentence.

1. Africa is (bigger, biggest) than Australia.

2. Asia is the (bigger, biggest) continent.

3. Australia is (smaller, smallest) than Africa.

4. Australia is the (smaller, smallest) continent.

5. Asia is (bigger, biggest) than Australia.

■ Write <u>bigger</u> or <u>biggest</u> in the blanks to make each sentence correct.

1. Asia is the _____ continent.

2. Asia is _____ than the continent of Africa.

3. Africa is _____ than the continent of Australia.

ELD Standard
    Locate and identify the function of text features such as format, diagrams, charts, glossaries, and indexes.
ELA Standard
    Interpret information from diagrams, charts, and graphs.

67

■ Write <u>smaller</u> or <u>smallest</u> in the blanks to make each sentence correct.

1. Africa is _____ than the continent of Asia.

2. Australia is _____ than the continent of Africa.

3. Australia is the _____ continent.

■ Use the information in the table to compare the continents.

Europe is bigger than Australia.
Australia is smaller than Antarctica.

Continent	Area in square miles (rounded to the nearest million)
Africa	12,000,000
Antarctica	6,000,000
Asia	17,000,000
Australia	3,000,000
Europe	4,000,000
North America	9,000,000
South America	7,000,000

1. _____

2. _____

3. _____

4. _____

Name   Date

ⓐ Asking and Answering Questions
Interpreting Information from a Chart

- Read the passage to a partner. Switch roles.

- Look at the map below and the continent chart on page 70.

- Ask and answer the questions with a partner.
  Use a complete sentence to answer the questions. Switch roles.

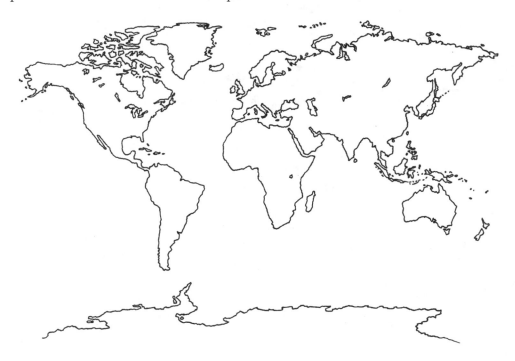

Continents of the World

Our world has seven continents. The seven continents are
Asia, Africa, North America, South America, Europe, Australia, and
Antarctica. The United States is on the continent of North
America. North America is the world's third largest continent.
The world's largest continent is Asia. Africa is the world's second
largest continent. Australia is the world's smallest continent.

ELD Standard
   Ask and answer questions using phrases or simple sentences. Locate and identify the function of text features such as
   format, diagrams, charts, glossaries, and indexes.
ELA Standard
   Understand how text features (e.g., format, graphics, sequence, diagrams, illustrations, charts, maps) make information
   accessible and usable.

Continent	Size 1 = largest 7 = smallest	Native Animals	Important Fact	Industry
Australia	smallest (7)	kangaroos, koala bears	native people = Aborigines	wool
Africa	second largest (2)	zebras, lions, tigers, elephants	largest city = Cairo	coffee, coconut, oil
Antarctica	fifth largest (5)	tiny insects, seals, penguins, polar bears	surrounded by oceans	tourism
Asia	world's largest (1)	orangutans, Sumatran rhinos, sloth bears	most mountainous continent	rice, oil
North America	third largest (3)	buffalo	largest Native American groups, Cherokee, Navajo	wheat, cattle, corn, cotton
South America	fourth largest (4)	rain forest animals, three-toed sloths, jaguars	Native Americans, Incas, Mayas	bananas, coffee, sugar
Europe	sixth largest (6)	cows, sheep	There are many countries in Europe.	vegetables, dairy products, oil, minerals

■ Answer the questions with a partner. Use the information on pages 69 and 70 to help you.

■ Use complete sentences for your answers.

1. What are the seven continents of the world?
   List the seven continents from smallest to largest.

   _____

   _____

   _____

2. What is one industry of Africa? _____

3. What are the native animals of Australia? _____

4. What is the largest continent in the world? _____

5. What is the smallest continent in the world? _____

   _____

6. What is one important fact about the continent of Asia? _____

   _____

7. What is one important fact about Europe? _____

   _____

8. What continent has the buffalo as a native animal? _____

   _____

9. What is the most mountainous continent? _____

10. What is the continent surrounded by oceans? _____

   _____

Name   Date

◧ Demonstrating Listening Comprehension

■ Read the passage to a partner. Your partner *sums up*. Switch roles.

Maylee, The Ocean Diver

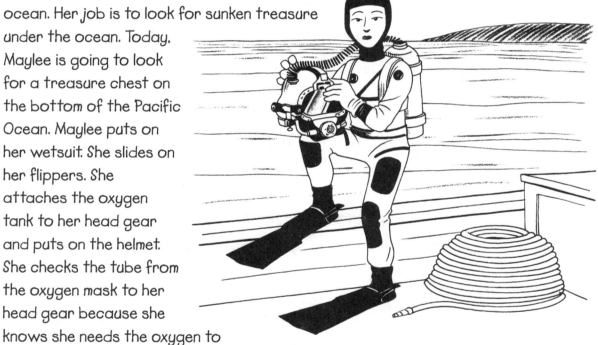

Maylee is a diver. She lives in San Clemente, California. Maylee dives off boats into the ocean. Her job is to look for sunken treasure under the ocean. Today, Maylee is going to look for a treasure chest on the bottom of the Pacific Ocean. Maylee puts on her wetsuit. She slides on her flippers. She attaches the oxygen tank to her head gear and puts on the helmet. She checks the tube from the oxygen mask to her head gear because she knows she needs the oxygen to breathe. Maylee dives off the boat. First, she picks up something shiny and yellow. Then she picks up something rough and pink. The next think she picks up is purple and soft. Maylee sees something that is a bright green. She picks it up. Maylee finds something black and glossy. She picks that up too. Finally, she picks up something iridescent orange. It is so big that Maylee cannot hold it.

ELD Standard
Respond orally to simple stories by answering factual comprehension questions, using phrases or simple sentences.
ELA Standard
Analyze text that is organized in sequential and chronological order. Use organizational features of printed text to locate relevant information.

- Make a mind map for the things Maylee sees on the bottom of the ocean.
- List the object under the color.
- Consult the links in the students' area of www.intensiveenglish.net to help you.

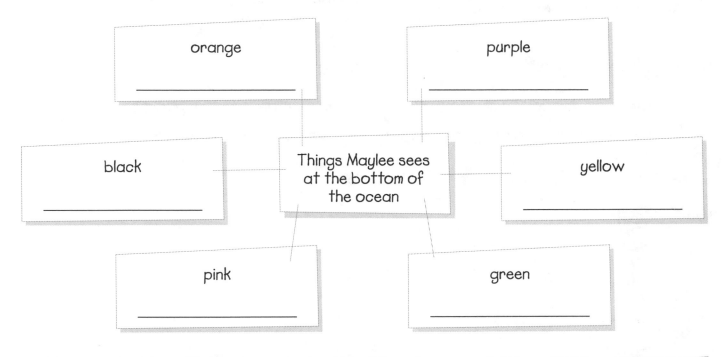

- Write six sentences telling what you think Maylee picks up off the bottom of the ocean. Read the sentences to a partner.

1. She picks up a shiny yellow _____

2. She picks up _____

3. She picks up _____

4. She picks up _____

5. She picks up _____

6. She picks up _____

Name _____   Date _____

b Word Families, Spelling Friends ch_, wh_

- Read the words on the right.
- Write the correct sentence next to each picture below.
- Read the sentences to a partner.

chip	chest	wheat
chunk	chin	whip
chipmunk	child	where
churn	whale	what
	white	

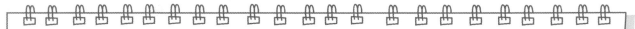

The lady is going to <u>ch</u>urn the butter.   :   Marcos likes to eat <u>wh</u>eat bread.

The policeman has a badge on his <u>ch</u>est.   :   <u>Wh</u>ere is the bus going?

1 _____

2 _____

3 _____

4 _____

74

ELD Standard
Recognize English phonemes that correspond to phonemes students already hear and produce while reading aloud.
ELA Standard
Spell roots, suffixes, prefixes, contractions, and syllabic constructions correctly.

Name   Date

ⓐ Demonstrating Listening Comprehension

The River
by Robert Louis Stevenson

Golden is the sand.

It flows along forever,

With trees on either hand,

Green leaves a-floating,

Castles on the foam,

Boats of mine a-boating,

When will all come home?

On goes the river

And out past the mill,

Away down the valley,

Away down the hill.

Away down the river,

A hundred miles or more,

Other little children

Shall bring my boats ashore.

1. The sand in the poem is —
   - ☐ gray
   - ☐ brown
   - ☐ golden
   - ☐ green

2. Which line from the poem lets you know that young people are close to the river?
   - ☐ It flows along forever.
   - ☐ Other little children shall bring my boats ashore.
   - ☐ And out past the mill.
   - ☐ A hundred miles or more.

ELD Standard
   Respond orally to simple stories by answering factual comprehension questions, using phrases or simple sentences.
ELA Standard
   Identify and analyze the characteristics of poetry.

3. Why does the author include the line "boats
   of mine a-boating"?
   - [ ] To tell how to sail a boat.
   - [ ] To explain how to fly.
   - [ ] To tell about sailing a boat on a river.
   - [ ] To tell about an ocean.

4. Who is the author of this poem?
   - [ ] Carl Sandberg
   - [ ] Louisa May Alcott
   - [ ] Shakespeare
   - [ ] Robert Louis Stevenson

5. What is the poem's setting?
   - [ ] the ocean
   - [ ] a forest
   - [ ] a river
   - [ ] a waterfall

6. On line 3, what does the word "hand" mean?
   - [ ] finger
   - [ ] bank
   - [ ] current
   - [ ] tributary

7. Write three sentences about the boat's trip down the river. Read your sentences to a partner.

   A. _____

   _____

   B. _____

   _____

   C. _____

   _____

Name _____   Date _____

b Descriptive Writing

Writing Prompt

▪ Describe a river.

Before Writing: Make a mind map, using words that describe the river.

After Writing: Read your description to a partner.

The River

by _____

The river looks _____

_____

The river feels _____

_____

The river smells _____

_____

The river sounds _____

_____

The river tastes like _____

_____

ELD Standard
Create simple sentences, or phrases, with some assistance. Use models to write short narratives.

ELA Standard
Write responses to literature.

Name _____   Date _____

◧ Contractions with Verbs

▬ ▬ ▬ ▬ ▬ ▬ ▬ ▬ ▬ ▬ ▬ ▬ ▬ ▬ ▬ ▬ ▬ ▬ ▬ ▬

Contractions

✔ A <u>contraction</u> is a word made from two words.

✔ A contraction can be made by combining a subject pronoun with a verb.

▬ ▬ ▬ ▬ ▬ ▬ ▬ ▬ ▬ ▬ ▬ ▬ ▬ ▬ ▬ ▬ ▬ ▬ ▬ ▬

I will/I'll	*she has/she's*	*it is/it's*	*I have/I've*
they will/they'll	*you have/you've*	*we had/we'd*	*it will/it'll*

▬ ▬ ▬ ▬ ▬ ▬ ▬ ▬ ▬ ▬ ▬ ▬ ▬ ▬ ▬ ▬ ▬ ▬ ▬ ▬

▪ Write a contraction for the underlined words in each sentence.

▪ Read the sentences to a partner.

1. <u>She has</u> been to the desert. _____

2. <u>It is</u> very hot and dry in the desert. _____

3. <u>You have</u> seen an oasis, haven't you? _____

4. <u>We had</u> traveled to see the stone formations in the deserts of southern Utah.

   _____

5. <u>They will</u> plant cacti in the sand. _____

6. <u>It will</u> be hottest at noon in the desert. _____

7. <u>I will</u> be making my annual visit to the Sonoran Desert this winter. _____

8. Grandpa said, "<u>I have</u> seen many sandstorms in my life." _____

ELD Standard
   Spell correctly one-syllable words that have blends, contractions, compounds, and orthographic patterns.
ELA Standard
   Spell roots, suffixes, prefixes, contractions, and syllabic constructions correctly.

Name _____   Date _____

ⓐ Demonstrating Listening Comprehension
Word Families, Spelling Friends _ar, _arm

- Read the passage to a partner. Your partner *sums up*. Switch roles.
- Fill in the bubble for each correct answer.

Forest Rules

Ana is a forest ranger. She works in the Angeles National Forest, not far from Los Angeles, California. Ana's job is to watch over the forest in order to keep people, animals, and trees safe. Ana makes sure no one harms the forest. For example, she checks campfires. Ana knows that a flick of a match can start a big forest fire. Whenever there's a fire, Ana sounds a fire alarm and calls the fire department. She enforces the forest rules to keep the forest safe for animals, trees and people.

Forest Rules
1. Do not throw matches in the forest.
2. Use water to completely put out campfires.
3. Hike only on marked or designated trails.
4. Do not feed forest animals.
5. Do not hurt the wildlife.
6. Keep your campsite only in designated areas.

1. These rules tell how to —
   - ☐ keep the beach safe
   - ☐ keep your home safe
   - ☐ keep the forest safe
   - ☐ keep the city safe

2. You will need rule two only if you —
   - ☐ pitch a tent
   - ☐ feed the animals
   - ☐ go hiking
   - ☐ make a campfire

ELD Standard
Respond orally to simple stories by answering factual questions, using phrases or simple sentences. Recognize English phonemes that correspond to phonemes students already hear and produce while reading aloud.

ELA Standard
Draw inferences, conclusions, or generalizations about text and support them with textual evidence and prior knowledge. Spell roots, suffixes, prefixes, contractions, and syllabic constructions correctly.

3. Where do the rules tell you to hike?
   - [ ] next to redwood trees
   - [ ] on marked or designated trails
   - [ ] on highways
   - [ ] on green sidewalks

4. You do not need the rule to hike in designated areas if —
   - [ ] you don't go hiking
   - [ ] you don't go swimming
   - [ ] you don't make a campfire
   - [ ] you don't like animals

5. Which of these is one way to follow rule #4?
   - [ ] use the food for people to eat only.
   - [ ] use the food only for bears.
   - [ ] use the food only for small animals.
   - [ ] use the food only for squirrels.

6. Hike only in designated areas. <u>Designated</u> means —
   - [ ] destroyed
   - [ ] marked
   - [ ] detours
   - [ ] dangerous

- Read each word. Then fill out the chart.
- Read the sentences to a partner.

Word	Noun or Verb	Sentence
j<u>ar</u>		
c<u>ar</u>		
st<u>ar</u>		
sc<u>ar</u>		
h<u>arm</u>		
f<u>arm</u>		
ch<u>arm</u>		
al<u>arm</u>		

Name _____   Date _____

a Pronouns

— —

Use of Pronouns to Take the Place of Nouns

Maria lives in the rain forest.	_She_ lives in the rain forest.
Bob lives in the rain forest.	_He_ lives in the rain forest.
Bob and I live in the rain forest.	_We_ live in the rain forest.
Bob and Maria live in the rain forest.	_They_ live in the rain forest.

— —

▪ Draw a line under the pronouns.

1. He lives in the rain forest.

2. It is a monkey.

3. Where is she going?

4. We are going to visit the rain forest.

5. They are brothers.

— —

▪ In each sentence, replace the noun with a pronoun using the words on the chalkboard. Rewrite the sentences using the pronouns.

1. <u>Tall trees</u> grow in the emergent layer of the rain forest. _____

_____

2. <u>Mrs. Marshall</u> likes to eat the nuts and berries that grow in the rain forest. _____

_____

ELD Standard
   Write an increasing number of words and simple sentences appropriate for language arts and other content areas.
ELA Standard
   Identify and correctly use verbs, modifiers, nouns and pronouns.

3. <u>Mike</u> watches the orangutan play in the sun. _____

_____

4. <u>Flowers</u> grow under the canopy. _____

_____

5. <u>Tigers</u> are part of the cat family. _____

_____

6. <u>Kiwi</u> spends the day asleep under the undergrowth on the forest floor. _____

_____

7. <u>A sun bear</u> is a very small bear that likes honey. _____

_____

8. Can you see <u>the rosewood tree</u>? _____

_____

9. <u>Some people in the rain forest</u> live in huts. _____

_____

10. <u>Paul and Pamela</u> build furniture made of teak. _____

_____

11. <u>Cindy</u> sees a pink-toed tarantula in the rain forest. _____

_____

12. <u>Peter and I</u> want to sail a boat on the Amazon River. _____

_____

Name _____   Date _____

a Demonstrating Listening Comprehension
Word Families, Spelling Friends _eigh, _eight

▪ Read the questions on the next page to a partner. Then read the passage together. Underline the words with _eigh_ or _eight_.

▪ Answer the questions.

The word *tundra* is a Russian word that means a treeless, marshy area. The Arctic tundra stretches three million square miles across the northern portions of Alaska, Canada, Greenland, Russia, Norway, Sweden, and Finland. The Arctic tundra is a cold and isolated place.

During the winter, the ground is frozen. The winters are long and very dark. Some animals that live in the tundra, like the polar bear, have thick fur and an extra layer of fat to keep warm. They gain weight to help them survive the winter. Emperor penguins use their feathers to keep warm. They live in groups and huddle together for warmth.

Summer in the Arctic tundra lasts about two months, and the sun never sets. Summers often have strong winds. The surface soil in the summer tundra is very delicate. In places without roads, the tracks from trucks and other vehicles can damage the thawed soil. To help protect the environment, people and freight are carried on special vehicles that do not leave large tracks.

The inhabitants of the Arctic tundra include the Inuit in Alaska, Canada, and Greenland, the Suomi, or Lapps, in the Scandinavian nations, and the Yakuts, Chukchi, and Samoyeds in Russia. Their neighbors, western people from farther south, also live and work in the Arctic region.

ELD Standard
Respond orally to simple stories by answering factual comprehension questions using phrases or simple sentences. Recognize English phonemes that correspond to phonemes students already hear and produce while reading aloud. Use correct parts of speech.

ELA Standard
Use knowledge of author's purpose to comprehend information in the text. Read common word families. Spell basic short-vowel, r-controlled, and consonant-blend patterns correctly. Identify and correctly use various parts of speech, including nouns and verbs, in writing and speaking.

1. <u>Tundra</u> means —
   ☐ treeless, marshy area
   ☐ sunshine
   ☐ grasslands
   ☐ wetlands

2. What does the author want to say?
   ☐ Animals and people like living in the Arctic tundra.
   ☐ Animals and people adapt to living in the Arctic tundra.
   ☐ The Arctic tundra is at the top of the world.
   ☐ The Arctic tundra is a great place to live.

3. During the winter, the ground in the Arctic tundra is —
   ☐ green
   ☐ soft
   ☐ brown
   ☐ hard

4. Emperor penguins huddle together for —
   ☐ warmth
   ☐ walking
   ☐ strength
   ☐ protection

- Read the words on the chart. Discuss whether the words are nouns or verbs.
- Fill in the chart. Read the sentences to a partner.

Word	Noun or Verb	Sentence
weigh		
sleigh		
neighbor		
freight		
weight		
eight		

Name _____ Date _____

a Demonstrating Listening Comprehension
Capitalization

▬ ▬ ▬ ▬ ▬ ▬ ▬ ▬ ▬ ▬ ▬ ▬ ▬ ▬ ▬ ▬ ▬ ▬ ▬

■ Read the passage together. *Sum up* what the passage is about.

Grasslands

Grass covers the land in some places of the world. These places are called grasslands. Grasslands have grass for thousands and thousands of miles but there are very few trees. There are grasslands on many of the continents of the world, including Africa, North America, Australia and Asia.

Many animals live in the grasslands. The grass provides food for the animals. Some animals on the continent of Africa live in the grasslands. Many different kinds of animals can live together in the grasslands of Africa because they eat different parts of the grass. Striped zebra eat the top of the grass while antelopes eat the short grass near the ground. The animals that eat the grass become the food for meat-eating grassland animals, such as the lion. Small animals dig holes underground so they can dive to safety when they see the lion. Other animals that live on the African grasslands include buffalo, elephants, leopards and cheetahs.

The grasslands of North America are home for bison herds, cattle, mule deer, coyotes and wolves. These animals move across the grasslands so they always have fresh grass to eat.

Kangaroos make their home on the continent of Australia. Deer and jaguars also make their home on grasslands in Australia.

ELD Standard
  Respond orally to simple stories by answering factual comprehension questions, using phrases or simple sentences.
  Use capital letters to begin proper nouns.
ELA Standard
  Understand how text features (e.g., format, graphics, sequence, diagrams, illustrations, charts, maps) make information accessible and usable. Use correct capitalization.

■ Label each continent. The names of continents begin with a capital letter.

■ Place these animals on the continent where they live in the grasslands.

leopards	antelope	cheetahs
bison herds	deer	kangaroos
zebra	lions	coyotes
cattle	buffalo	jaguars
	elephants	wolves

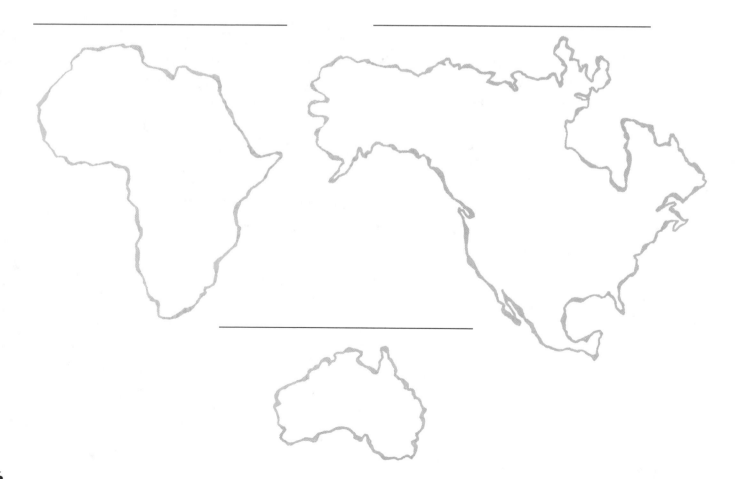

Name _____   Date _____

a Commas

✔ Use commas to separate three or more items in a series.

Fresh water wetlands are found at the edges of lakes, ponds, streams and rivers.

✔ Use a comma between a word and its explanation.

We saw a great white heron, a type of bird that lives in the Everglades National Park.

✔ Use a comma before and after an explanation.

George Washington, the first president of the United States, was born in Virginia.

■ In each group, find the sentence that has commas in all the right places.

1. ☐ The wetlands include marshes, swamps, bogs and mud flats.
   ☐ The wetlands include marshes, swamps bogs and mud flats.
   ☐ The wetlands include marshes swamps bogs and mud flats.

2. ☐ People animals, and plants, live in a habitat.
   ☐ People animals and plants live in a habitat.
   ☐ People, animals and plants live in a habitat.

3. ☐ Swamps have many plants that decay or rot.
   ☐ Swamps have many plants that decay, or rot.
   ☐ Swamps have many plants, that decay or rot.

4. ☐ My friend Jamal, the boy with the green shirt, is from Mississippi.
   ☐ My friend Jamal, the boy with the green shirt is from Mississippi.
   ☐ My friend Jamal the boy with the green shirt, is from Mississippi.

■ Write the sentences over correctly. Put in the commas where they are needed.

1. Tenochtitlan the capital city of the Aztecs was built on a lake.

_____

2. There are trees animals bugs and flowers in the forest.

_____

ELD Standard
   Use some commas appropriately.
ELA Standard
   Identify and correctly use prepositional phrases, appositives, and independent and dependent clauses.

Name _____   Date _____

ⓐ Subject Pronouns

▬ ▬

✔ A <u>pronoun</u> is a word that takes the place of one or more nouns.

Geographers use climate to divide an area into regions.

They use climate to divide an area into regions.

✔ Use a <u>subject pronoun</u> as the subject of a sentence.

<u>Subject pronouns</u> are *I, you, he, she, it, we* and *they*.

▬ ▬

▪ Rewrite each sentence changing the underlined subject to a subject pronoun.

▪ Read your sentences to a partner.

1. <u>Mark</u> lives in a region along the coastline of the United States.

   _____

2. <u>Mountains and plains</u> are two landforms found in the United States.

   _____

3. <u>Louisa</u> lives in the Appalachian Mountains, the second longest mountain range in the U.S.

   _____

   _____

4. <u>Bill and I</u> are going to visit the Rocky Mountains in Utah and Colorado.

   _____

5. Didn't <u>you and Jacob</u> visit the Great Lakes region last year?

   _____

6. <u>Death Valley</u> has the lowest, hottest, driest location in North America.

   _____

ELD Standard
Use correct parts of speech including correct subject/verb agreement.
ELA Standard
Identify and correctly use verbs that are often misused, modifiers, and pronouns.

Name _____   Date _____

b Alphabetizing

✔ Reference sources, such as telephone directories, almanacs, dictionaries, encyclopedias, and thesauri, are organized alphabetically. Look at the first letter of the word.

eastern, southern
The letter e comes before the letter s.
The word eastern comes before the word southern in alphabetical order.

✔ If two words begin with the same letter, look at the second letter of the word.

western, warm
The letter a comes before the letter e.
The word warm comes before the word western in alphabetical order.

✔ If two different words begin with the same letters, compare the words letter by letter until you find the difference.

geography, geographer
The letter e comes before the letter y.
The word geographer comes before the word geography in alphabetical order.

✔ If two 2-word terms have the same first word, look at the second word in each term to decide alphabetical order.

mountain peak, mountain range
The letter p comes before the letter r.
The term mountain peak comes before the term mountain range in alphabetical order.

■ Write the following places in alphabetical order: Lake Ontario, Pennsylvania, Lake Erie, Mississippi, Colorado, Lake Okeechobee, Missouri, Louisiana

1. _____   5. _____

2. _____   6. _____

3. _____   7. _____

4. _____   8. _____

ELD Standard
Arrange words in alphabetical order.
ELA Standard
Arrange words in alphabetical order. Use organizational features of printed text to locate relevant information.

Name _____   Date _____

◘ Object Pronouns

— —

✔ A <u>pronoun</u> is a word that takes the place of one or more nouns.

✔ Use an <u>object pronoun</u> as the object of a sentence.

The movie was created by a *Hollywood screenwriter.*
The movie was created by *her.*

✔ Object pronouns are *me, you, him, her, it, us* and *them.*

— —

▪ Rewrite each sentence, changing the underlined noun to an object pronoun.

▪ Read your sentences to a partner.

1. Trees need <u>water and good soil</u> to survive.

   _____

2. In the mountains, carpenters use <u>the wood from pine trees</u> to build houses.

   _____

3. The Gulf Coast region provides <u>you and me</u> with oil.

   _____

4. Ranchers get <u>water</u> from wells.

   _____

5. The doctor examined <u>the sick girl</u>.

   _____

6. Antonio is a chef who works at the Grand Hotel with <u>John</u>.

   _____

7. Geologists found <u>oil</u> in Alaska.

   _____

ELD Standard
   Use correct parts of speech, including correct subject/verb agreement.
ELA Standard
   Identify and correctly use verbs that are often misused, modifiers, and pronouns.

Name _____   Date _____

b Prepositions

▬ ▬

✔ A preposition is a word that relates a person or object with another word.
Some prepositions are *behind*, *on*, *for*, *at*, *in*, *with*, *from* and *to*.

✔ Sometimes an object pronoun is used after a preposition.
The man <u>behind me</u> is my uncle.

▬ ▬

▪ Rewrite each sentence, changing the underlined noun to an object pronoun.

▪ Circle the preposition that precedes each object pronoun.

▪ Read your sentences to a partner.

Example: Our community's natural resources are useful to <u>all citizens</u>.
Our community's natural resources are useful (to) us.

1. The children sometimes rode on <u>the neighbor's horse</u>.

_____

2. Mark produces furniture for <u>you and me</u>.

_____

3. To make extra money, Esperanza sews clothes for <u>my sister Maria</u>.

_____

4. Oil is an important natural resource to <u>workers in Louisiana</u>.

_____

5. Are you looking at <u>Bob</u>? What is he doing?

_____

6. The business person is going to meet with <u>the banker</u>.

_____

ELD Standard
Use correct parts of speech, including correct subject/verb agreement.

ELA Standard
Identify and correctly use verbs that are often misused, modifiers, and pronouns.

Name   Date

ⓐ Interpreting Charts and Maps

- ▪ Use the map and map keys on pages 93 and 94 to answer the questions below.
- ▪ Answer all questions in complete sentences.
- ▪ Read your answers to a partner.

1. What states in the Pacific West region are having rainy weather?

    _____

2. What state in the New England region is experiencing snowy weather?

    _____

3. What will the skies look like in Mississippi and Georgia?

    _____

4. What state is having thunderstorms?

    _____

5. What state has the highest temperature? What state has the coldest temperature?

    _____

6. Which region in the United States has the warmest weather?

    _____

7. Are all the sunny states warm?

    _____

8. List the states that have snow and a temperature below 20 degrees Fahrenheit.

    _____

ELD Standard
 Read and orally identify text features such as titles, tables of contents, chapter headings, diagrams, charts, glossaries, and indexes in written text.
ELA Standard
 Understand how text features (e.g., format, graphics, sequence, diagrams, illustrations, charts, maps) make information accessible and usable.

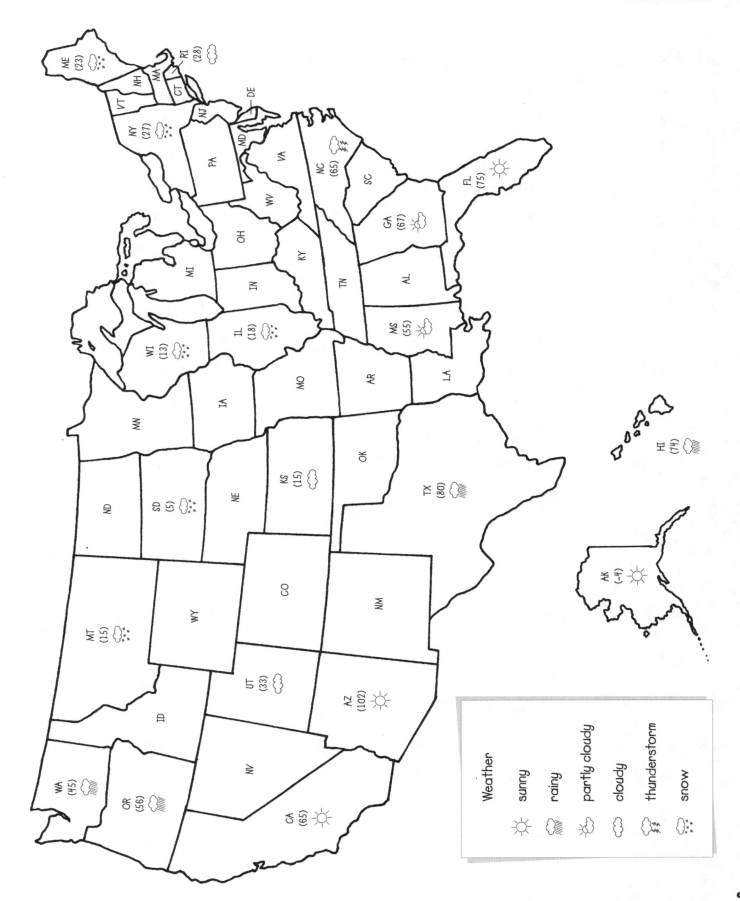

Weather

☀ sunny

🌧 rainy

⛅ partly cloudy

☁ cloudy

⛈ thunderstorm

🌨 snow

Region	State	Abbrev.
Midwest	North Dakota	ND
	South Dakota	SD
	Nebraska	NE
	Kansas	KS
	Minnesota	MN
	Iowa	IA
	Missouri	MO
	Wisconsin	WI
	Illinois	IL
	Michigan	MI
	Indiana	IN
	Ohio	OH
Southeast	Arkansas	AR
	Louisiana	LA
	Mississippi	MS
	Alabama	AL
	Georgia	GA
	South Carolina	SC
	North Carolina	NC
	Virginia	VA
	West Virginia	WV
	Maryland	MD
	Kentucky	KY
	Tennessee	TN
	Florida	FL

Region	State	Abbrev.
Mt. West	Nevada	NV
	Idaho	ID
	Montana	MT
	Wyoming	WY
	Utah	UT
	Colorado	CO
Southwest	Arizona	AZ
	New Mexico	NM
	Texas	TX
	Oklahoma	OK
Mid Atlantic	Pennsylvania	PA
	New York	NY
	Delaware	DE
	New Jersey	NJ
New England	Vermont	VT
	Maine	ME
	New Hampshire	NH
	Massachusetts	MA
	Connecticut	CT
	Rhode Island	RI
Pacific West	California	CA
	Oregon	OR
	Washington	WA
	Alaska	AK
	Hawaii	HI

Name _____   Date _____

a Demonstrating Comprehension

- Read the passage and poem to a partner. Your partner sums up what the poem is mainly about. Switch roles.

- On the next page, answer the questions. Draw a picture and write a summary of what the poem is mainly about.

Robert Frost was a famous poet who spent many years of his life in the New England region, specifically in the states of New Hampshire and Vermont. Many of Robert Frost's poems are about New England's beautiful landscape. Robert Frost "said" one of his poems at President John F. Kennedy's inauguration in January, 1961. Robert Frost's poetry has enriched the culture of the United States.

The Road Not Taken
Robert Frost

(1) Two roads diverged in a yellow wood,
     And sorry I could not travel both
     And be one traveler, long I stood
     And looked down as far as I could
     To where it bent in the undergrowth;

(2) Then took the other, as just as fair,
     And having perhaps the better claim,
     Because it was grassy and wanted wear;
     Though as for that the passing there
     Has worn them really about the same,

(3) And both that morning equally lay
     In leaves no step had trodden black.
     Oh, I kept the first for another day!
     Yet knowing how way leads on to way,
     I doubted if I should ever come back.

(4) I shall be telling this with a sigh
     Somewhere ages and ages hence:
     Two roads diverged in a wood, and I –
     I took the one less traveled by,
     And that has made all the difference.

ELD Standard
Read and orally identify the main idea and use them to draw inferences about written text using simple sentences.
ELA Standard
Discuss main ideas and concepts presented in text identifying and assessing evidence that support those ideas.

1. The speaker in the poem is faced with a —
   - [ ] new road
   - [ ] change of seasons
   - [ ] choice
   - [ ] friend

2. This poem is written to show —
   - [ ] how people make choices in life
   - [ ] how to travel on a busy road
   - [ ] how to rake leaves
   - [ ] how roads diverge

3. What mood has the poet created in this poem?
   - [ ] suspense
   - [ ] sadness
   - [ ] surprise
   - [ ] silliness

4. In the third stanza, the speaker describes —
   - [ ] how he can't travel on both roads
   - [ ] how he chose the road that was grassy
   - [ ] how the two roads looked
   - [ ] the undergrowth

5. In line one of the first stanza, the word "diverged" probably means —
   - [ ] returned
   - [ ] walked
   - [ ] divided
   - [ ] traveled

6. There is enough information in this poem to show that —
   - [ ] the speaker didn't choose a road
   - [ ] the speaker chose the first road
   - [ ] the roads were wet and extremely slippery
   - [ ] the speaker chose the less traveled road

7. What U.S. region did Robert Frost frequently write about?
   - [ ] Midwest
   - [ ] Southwest
   - [ ] New England
   - [ ] Cajun Country

8. The author uses the word *wood* two times. What does it mean?
   - [ ] building material
   - [ ] tree
   - [ ] forest
   - [ ] path

Name _____   Date _____

b Writing Application: Analyzing Poetry

▪ Answer the following questions with a partner. Read your answer to a partner. Switch roles.

1. At the beginning of the poem on page 95, the speaker is faced with a choice between

   two roads. Which choice does he make? _____

   _____

2. What reason does the speaker give for making that choice? _____

   _____

   _____

3. Find the lines that tell that the speaker accepted his choice. _____

   _____

   _____

4. Explain what the poem is about. _____

   _____

5. A proverb says, "Life is a road of endless choices." Explain what this means in relation to

   the poem. _____

   _____

6. Describe a choice you have made. _____

   _____

ELD Standard
   Independently write simple responses to literature.
ELA Standard
   Write responses to literature. Demonstrate understanding of a literary work. Support judgments through references to
   the text and to prior knowledge.

Name   Date
_____   _____

a Demonstrating Comprehension

- Read the passage to a partner.
- Partner sums up after each paragraph. Switch roles.
- Answer the questions.
- Review your answers with a partner.

New York is in the Middle Atlantic Region of the United States. New York is famous for many landmarks. One of the most important is the Statue of Liberty.

The Statue of Liberty

(1) In New York harbor stands one of the most recognized figures in the world—the Statue of Liberty. This 150-foot-tall statue, a gift from the people of France to the citizens of America, honored the 1876 centennial celebration, America's one-hundredth birthday.

(2) The statue, a creation by Frederic Auguste Bartholdi, was first assembled in Paris in 1884. It has wrought-iron framework designed by Gustav Eiffel, who also designed the Eiffel Tower in Paris. After being assembled, it was disassembled and shipped across the Atlantic Ocean. The Statue of Liberty was then completely reassembled on a base planned by Richard Morris Hunt, a noted American architect.

(3) The Statue of Liberty and its base were paid for in an unusual way—without government help. Instead, the people of France made contributions for the statue and the people of America made contributions for the base. Among the contributors were many school children who took great pride in knowing that their pennies helped to build such a wonderful monument.

(4) Even though the outside of the Statue of Liberty is made of copper, it does not appear copper-colored. Over the years, exposure to the air has turned the copper a bluish-green color, which is known as verdigris.

ELD Standard
Read and orally identify the main ideas and use them to draw inferences about written text using simple sentences.
ELA Standard
Discern main ideas and concepts presented in texts, identifying and assessing evidence that support those ideas. Use quotation marks around the titles of poems.

(5) On October 26, 1886, the *Statue of Liberty* was unveiled in its permanent location in New York harbor. On its base is a plaque with "The New Colossus," a poem written by *Emma Lazarus* welcoming immigrants to the new land. Two lines near the end of the poem summarize the statue's spirit: *Give me your tired, your poor, your huddled masses yearning to breathe free.* Thousands of people were at the unveiling and, since then, millions have visited this symbol of freedom.

1. What makes the Statue of Liberty different from many other monuments?
   - ☐ It celebrates freedom.
   - ☐ It was paid for by the people of two countries, not the government.
   - ☐ It is much taller than any other monument.
   - ☐ It was made by a French sculptor.

2. Based on what you read in the passage, when was the United States born?
   - ☐ 1776
   - ☐ 1876
   - ☐ 1884
   - ☐ 1886

3. Why did school children of America feel proud of the Statue of Liberty?
   - ☐ They contributed money to help build the statue.
   - ☐ They contributed money to help send a ship to the United States.
   - ☐ They had a contest to pick the poem for the base.
   - ☐ They contributed money to help build the base.

4. Who wrote the poem on the plaque at the base of the Statue of Liberty?
   - ☐ Gustav Eiffel
   - ☐ Richard Hunt
   - ☐ Frederic Bartholdi
   - ☐ Emma Lazarus

5. The author included the second paragraph to tell why —
   - ☐ the Statue of Liberty had to be disassembled and reassembled
   - ☐ the copper skin on the Statue of Liberty was beginning to turn green
   - ☐ the Statue of Liberty was a gift to the American people for the centennial
   - ☐ the people of Paris wanted to see the Statue of Liberty first

6. In order to answer question 5, the best thing to do is —
   - ☐ reread the last sentence of each paragraph
   - ☐ reread the second paragraph
   - ☐ think about the story's main idea
   - ☐ reread the title

7. In paragraph 5, why does "The New Colossus" appear with quotation marks?
   - ☐ Emma Lazarus wrote many poems. One poem is called "The New Colossus."
   - ☐ "The New Colossus" is a very famous poem.
   - ☐ Whenever the name of a poem is used in an article or story, it needs to appear in quotation marks.
   - ☐ The poem appears on the Statue of Liberty.

Name _____   Date _____

b Writing Application: Making an Outline

- Write an outline to show the main idea and supporting details of each paragraph.
- Write a summary on a separate sheet of paper. Use the writing checklist at the back of the book to edit your work.

I. _____

   A. _____

   B. _____

II. _____

   A. _____

   B. _____

III. _____

   A. _____

   B. _____

IV. _____

   A. _____

V. _____

   A. _____

   B. _____

ELD Standard
Independently create cohesive paragraphs that develop a central idea.
ELA Standard
Edit and revise manuscript to improve the meaning and focus of writing.

Name   Date

a Demonstrating Comprehension

- Read the paragraph and recipe to a partner.
- Partner sums up. Switch roles.
- Answer the questions on page 102.
- Review your answers with a partner.

Delicious Southern Fried Chicken

Have you ever tasted Grandma's southern fried chicken? It is the best chicken in the whole state of Georgia. Grandma makes the chicken every Sunday. She gets fresh chicken from the farm. Then, she follows her famous southern fried chicken recipe.

Delicious Southern Fried Chicken

3 lbs. (pounds) chicken pieces, evenly sized
6 cups peanut oil for frying
paper towels
lemon or lime wedges (optional)

Coating Mix

1 1/2 cups all-purpose flour
1 1/2 teaspoons salt
1 teaspoon ground white pepper
2 teaspoons paprika (hot or mild)
2 teaspoons chicken seasoning mix

Cream Gravy (optional)

3 tablespoons frying oil
3 tablespoons all-purpose flour
1 cup whole milk
salt to taste

Steps

1. Soak chicken pieces in water for twenty minutes. Then, drain and pat with paper towels.
2. Make the coating by putting the flour, salt, pepper, paprika and chicken seasoning mix in a plastic bag.
3. Seal the bag and shake well.
4. Add chicken pieces to the bag and shake well.
5. Arrange the chicken pieces on a pan.
6. Chill uncovered in the refrigerator for 20 minutes.
7. Put in preheated oven at 350 degrees for 20 minutes.
8. Remove the chicken from the oven and fry in batches of 5 – 6 pieces for 8 – 10 minutes or until the chicken is golden brown.
9. If making the gravy, heat the oil in a saucepan and stir in the flour until it bubbles but is not brown.
10. Gradually stir in milk and salt to taste.

ELD Standard
Read and orally identify examples of fact/opinion and cause/effect in literature and content areas.
ELA Standard
Distinguish facts, supported inferences and opinions in text.

1. Which of these is a fact stated in this article?
   - ☐ You must soak the chicken pieces in water for 20 minutes.
   - ☐ Grandma's chicken is the best chicken in the state of Georgia.
   - ☐ Chicken is the healthiest food to eat.
   - ☐ Only the legs of the chicken are used in this recipe.

2. How many pound of chicken do you need for this recipe?
   - ☐ two pounds (lbs.)
   - ☐ three pounds (lbs.)
   - ☐ four pounds (lbs.)
   - ☐ seven pounds (lbs.)

3. Which sentence informs you that Grandma does not use frozen chicken in her recipe?
   - ☐ Add chicken pieces to the bag and shake well.
   - ☐ Then, she follows her famous southern fried chicken recipe.
   - ☐ It is the best chicken in the whole state of Georgia.
   - ☐ She gets fresh chicken from the farm.

4. One item that you don't have to do anything to is the —
   - ☐ coating mix
   - ☐ cream gravy
   - ☐ chicken
   - ☐ seasoning mix

5. After you make the coating, you should —
   - ☐ put it in the refrigerator
   - ☐ fry the chicken in batches of 5 – 6 pieces for 8 – 10 minutes
   - ☐ seal the bag and shake well
   - ☐ arrange the chicken pieces on a pan

6. When making the gravy, heat the oil in a saucepan and stir in the flour. Heat until it —
   - ☐ is smooth
   - ☐ bubbles
   - ☐ turns brown
   - ☐ turns white

7. The information in this article was written in order to —
   - ☐ tell where to buy southern fried chicken
   - ☐ give information about a new restaurant
   - ☐ give directions to Grandma's house
   - ☐ tell about Grandma's southern fried chicken and provide a tasty recipe

8. This recipe for chicken probably originated in the —
   - ☐ North
   - ☐ South
   - ☐ East
   - ☐ West

Name   Date

ⓐ Expository Writing

━ ━

Expository Writing

✔ Expository writing tells how to make or do something.

✔ Sometimes it is called "how to" writing.

✔ It tells the reader what to do and when to do it.

━ ━

There are many great recipes from the Midwest and Great Plains
regions. The Midwest is known for its agriculture. Kansas is known for
its premier grain production of corn in the east and wheat in the
west. Create a recipe using wheat, flour, corn or corn meal.

━ ━

Writing Prompt

▪ Create a recipe. On a separate sheet of paper, draw a picture of your prepared food. Entitle your drawing "My Finished Recipe."

Before Writing: Think about your recipe.
Break the recipe down into ingredients and steps.
Describe each step in the correct order.

After Writing: Use the writing checklist at the back of the book.
Read the steps to partner.

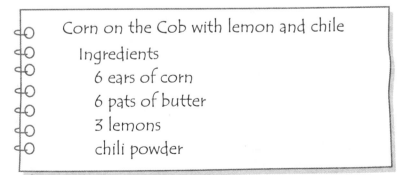

Corn on the Cob with lemon and chile
Ingredients
    6 ears of corn
    6 pats of butter
    3 lemons
    chili powder

ELD Standard
Write multi-paragraph narrative and expository compositions and examples appropriate for content areas with consistent use of standard grammar forms.
ELA Standard
Write a multi-paragraph expository composition.

A Recipe for _____

You will need:

_____   _____

_____   _____

_____   _____

_____   _____

Steps:

1. _____

2. _____

3. _____

4. _____

5. _____

6. _____

7. _____

8. _____

Name _____   Date _____

ⓐ Subject and Object Pronouns

✔ A <u>pronoun</u> is a word that takes the place of one or more nouns.

✔ Use a <u>subject pronoun</u> as the subject of a sentence.
  Subject pronouns are *I, you, he, she, it, we* and *they*.
  Maria jumps over the box.
  She jumps over the box.

✔ Use an <u>object pronoun</u> as the object of a sentence.
  Object pronouns are *me, you, him, her, it, us* and *them*.
  The teacher saw *Fernando and Pao* at the supermarket.
  The teacher saw *them* at the supermarket.

✔ You can use object pronouns after prepositions, such as *for, at, of, in, with* and *to*.
  Sara plays with us.

■ Circle the word in parentheses that correctly completes the sentence.
  Read the sentences to a partner.

1. (Them, They) went climbing in the Guadalupe Mountains of Texas.

2. (I, Me) think Texas has the most oil wells in the southwest region.

3. (We, Us) didn't know that farmers grow citrus fruit in Arizona.

4. We went to visit the Grand Canyon with (they, them).

5. (He, Him) was amazed at the rock formations in the desert near Sedona, Arizona.

6. It certainly sounds exciting to take a train to the Great Mesa with (she, her).

7. For (I, you) to feel comfortable riding a horse, it helps to ride a pony first.

8. He took the bus to Taos, New Mexico to buy silver jewelry with (I, me).

9. Marcos visited Oklahoma City and Tulsa with (they, them).

10. Ralph is going to drive with (we, us) from Albuquerque to Amarillo.

ELD Standard
  Use correct parts of speech including correct subject/verb agreement.
ELA Standard
  Identify and correctly use verbs that are often misused, modifiers, and pronouns.

Name   Date

b Using a Dictionary

✔ At the top of each page of the dictionary are two <u>guide words</u>.

  ▪ The first guide word is the first entry word on the page.

  ▪ The second word is the last entry word on that page.

---

test – Texan   **940**

Texan \tĕk-sən\ *adjective* **1**: relating to, or characteristic of, the state of Texas, or its inhabitants **2**: relating to the culture of Texas.

Texan *noun* **1**: person born in Texas **2**: person living in Texas **3**: the dialect of English spoken in Texas.

That man is Texan. Most inhabitants of Texas speak English with a Texan dialect.

✔ A dictionary can help you learn unfamiliar words. You can learn a word's

  ▪ meanings
  ▪ spellings
  ▪ part of speech
  ▪ pronunciation

✔ The entry words are arranged in alphabetical order. Read about alphabetizing on page 89.

ELD Standard
   Ask and answer questions using phrases or simple sentences.
ELA Standard
   Use a dictionary to learn the meaning and other features of unknown words. Use organizational features of printed text to locate relevant information.

■ Ask and answer the questions with a partner.

1. What is the first word that appears on this dictionary page? _____

2. What is the last word that appears on this dictionary page? _____

3. How many meanings does the word *Texan* have? _____
   Write the meanings.

   _____

   _____

   _____

   _____

   _____

4. How do the sentences at the bottom of the page help you with the word's meaning?

   _____

5. Write a sentence using the word *Texan*.

   _____

6. What parts of speech does the dictionary give for the word *Texan*?

   _____

7. In which state do Texans live? _____

8. What dialect do native inhabitants of Texas speak? _____

9. If you wanted to find the entry for Texas in this dictionary, what page would it probably

   be on? _____

Name   Date

ⓐ Demonstrating Comprehension

✔ A **fact** is a sentence that is true.

Farmers grow potatoes in Idaho.

✔ An **opinion** is what someone thinks.

Idaho has the best potatoes in the world.

■ Read the passage to a partner.

■ Answer the questions.

■ Review your answers with a partner.

Idaho is a state in the Mountain West region of the United States. Idaho is famous for its potatoes. Idaho has rich volcanic soil, water from melting mountain snow, warm days and cool nights, and clean air. All of these are perfect to grow potatoes.

Idaho Potato Art

Do you like to eat potatoes? Potatoes are great to eat mashed, fried or baked. The state of Idaho in the Mountain West region produces the best potatoes in the world! Potatoes are not only good to eat, but they are excellent print-makers. Have you ever heard of a potato initial stamp? Here's how you make a potato initial stamp.

You will need:

✔ one potato

✔ paring knife

✔ tempura paint

ELD Standard
    Read and orally identify examples of fact/opinion and cause/effect in literature and content areas.
ELA Standard
    Distinguish facts, supported inferences, and opinions in text.

Here's what you do:

1. Cut the potato in half and draw your initial on the cut area. You may want to use a letter pattern or a stencil.

2. Use the paring knife to cut away the potato that surrounds your initial. When your initial is standing out from the rest of the potato, your potato print block is ready.

3. Dip your potato into a small, flat dish of tempura paint and try it on a piece of paper until you get the right amount of paint. You can put these initial prints on your book covers or binders. You can even experiment with printing on cloth. Potato printing is the best way to print quickly.

1. Another good title for these directions is —
   ☐ The State of Idaho
   ☐ Potato Binders
   ☐ Potato Eating
   ☐ Potato Printing

2. Which of these is an opinion in the directions?
   ☐ Potato printing is the best way to print quickly.
   ☐ Cut the potatoes in half.
   ☐ Use a paring knife.
   ☐ Dip your potato in a small flat dish of tempura paint.

3. If the letter in the potato is not cut carefully, it —
   ☐ will not have enough paint
   ☐ will print easily
   ☐ will be hard to read
   ☐ will be soft

4. If you did not have a potato, you could probably use a —
   ☐ cookie
   ☐ turnip
   ☐ tomato
   ☐ cucumber

5. What do the directions say to use to cut the potato?
   ☐ a paring knife
   ☐ a steak knife
   ☐ scissors
   ☐ a pocket knife

6. Printing on cloth can be done as —
   ☐ a sewing technique
   ☐ a way to paint your house
   ☐ a short cut
   ☐ an experiment

Name _____   Date _____

ⓐ Subject–Verb Agreement

▬▬ ▬ ▬▬ ▬ ▬ ▬ ▬ ▬ ▬ ▬ ▬ ▬ ▬ ▬ ▬ ▬ ▬ ▬ ▬ ▬

✔ The verb must agree with the subject of a sentence.

✔ If the subject of a sentence is a singular noun or *he*, *she* or *it*, the verb must be singular.
The <u>tornado</u> <u>blows</u> the tree.

✔ If the subject is a plural noun, or *I*, *we*, *you* or *they*, the verb must be plural.
The windstorm<u>s</u> <u>occur</u> when hot air hits cold, dry air.

> **Rule**   If the subject ends in <u>s</u>, the verb can't end in <u>s</u>.
> *The tornadoe<u>s</u> blow.*
>
> If the verb ends in <u>s</u>, the subject can't end in <u>s</u>.
> *The <u>wind</u> blow<u>s</u>.*

▬▬ ▬ ▬▬ ▬ ▬ ▬ ▬ ▬ ▬ ▬ ▬ ▬ ▬ ▬ ▬ ▬ ▬ ▬ ▬ ▬

▪ Underline the correct verb in each sentence.

▪ Read the sentences to a partner.

1. The Pacific West region (consist, consists) of the states of Alaska, California, Hawaii, Oregon and Washington.
2. The movie producer (make, makes) his movies in Burbank, California.
3. Maria and Carlos (swim, swims) in the ocean at Waikiki Beach.
4. John and Sara (take, takes) a plane to Anchorage, Alaska every week.
5. Antonia (ski, skis) in the Cascade Mountains in Oregon.
6. Don (fish, fishes) for salmon in the Columbia River.
7. My brother often (drive, drives) from his apartment in Seattle to our house in Spokane.
8. The Iditarod is a famous dog sled race that (start, starts) in Anchorage and (end, ends) in Nome.

ELD Standard
Use parts of speech including correct subject/verb agreement.
ELA Standard
Identify and correctly use verbs that are often misused, modifiers, and pronouns.

■ Write the correct present tense verb in these sentences. Write the sentences over correctly.

1. Beavers _____ in the state of Oregon. (live)

   _____

   _____

2. John and Mary _____ on the Oregon Trail. (travel)

   _____

   _____

3. Farmers _____ tomatoes on farms in the California's Central Valley.
   (grow)

   _____

   _____

4. Martha and Carlos _____ apples grown in Washington. (eat)

   _____

   _____

Name _____   Date _____

ⓐ Demonstrating Comprehension

- Read the questions first.
- Read the passage to a partner. Your partner sums up after each paragraph. Switch roles.
- Answer the questions. Review your answers with a partner.

The First Americans

(1)   Have people always lived in the Americas? Many thousands of years ago, no one lived on the continents of North or South America. The first people who came to North America migrated from Asia. They came to North America between 20,000 and 36,000 years ago. About 36,000 years ago, there was land where the Bering Strait presently connects the continents of Asia and North America. The land bridge was over 1,000 miles wide.

(2)   People crossed into North America looking for plants and animals to eat. These people were called <u>nomads</u>. Nomads were people who wandered around looking for food. These nomads are referred to as the first Americans. Over the following millennia, groups of Native Americans moved south, all the way to today's *Tierra del Fuego*, the islands at the southern end of South America.

(3)   By 1492, the year that Christopher Columbus first reached the Americas, scientists estimate that there were between 50 and 100 million people in North America, South America and the Caribbean. There were hundreds of societies, both large and small, and around 500 distinct languages spoken. Some Native Americans developed political structures that were as sophisticated as any in Africa or Europe. Some Native Americans lived in ancient towns. Others were nomadic people who gathered or hunted food.

(4)   Native Americans developed advanced technologies to help them live. They used fish heads for fertilizer, knew about dangerous animals and poisonous plants, learned about making medicines from plants, and became experts in growing corn, squash, pumpkin, tomatoes, potatoes, and yams.

ELD Standard
   Read and orally identify the main ideas and use them to draw inferences about written text using simple sentences.
ELA Standard
   Discuss main ideas and concepts presented in text identifying and assessing evidence that supports those ideas.

1. How many years ago did the first people migrate to North America?
   - [ ] 10,000 – 30,000 years ago
   - [ ] 20,000 – 36,000 years ago
   - [ ] about 40,000 years ago
   - [ ] about 70,000 years ago

2. Who first came to North America?
   - [ ] people from the North Pole
   - [ ] Europeans
   - [ ] nomads
   - [ ] Africans

3. What is paragraph 2 mainly about?
   - [ ] why people came to the Americas
   - [ ] why people moved to Tierra del Fuego
   - [ ] how people came to the Americas
   - [ ] how Native Americans developed technologies to help them live

4. Why did groups of Americans move south?
   - [ ] to develop more languages
   - [ ] to look for more food sources
   - [ ] to learn about sophisticated political structures
   - [ ] to live in ancient towns

5. You would most likely find this article in a —
   - [ ] history book
   - [ ] science magazine
   - [ ] literature textbook
   - [ ] cookbook

6. The web below shows some important ideas in the article.

   Which of these belongs in the empty box?
   - [ ] weren't nomads
   - [ ] spoke around 500 distinct languages
   - [ ] grew wheat
   - [ ] came to the Americas millions of years ago

developed advanced technologies		came from Asia

   Native Americans

   | lived in large and small societies | | |

Writing Prompt

- Write a summary of this article including the main ideas and significant details on a separate sheet of paper.

  Before Writing: Complete the main idea mapping chart on the next page.

  After Writing: Use the writing checklist at the back of the book.

                  Have a partner use the writing checklist to edit your writing.

                  Read your summary to a partner.

Name　　　　　　　　　　　　　　　　　　　　　　Date

b Main Idea Mapping

Main Idea Mapping Chart

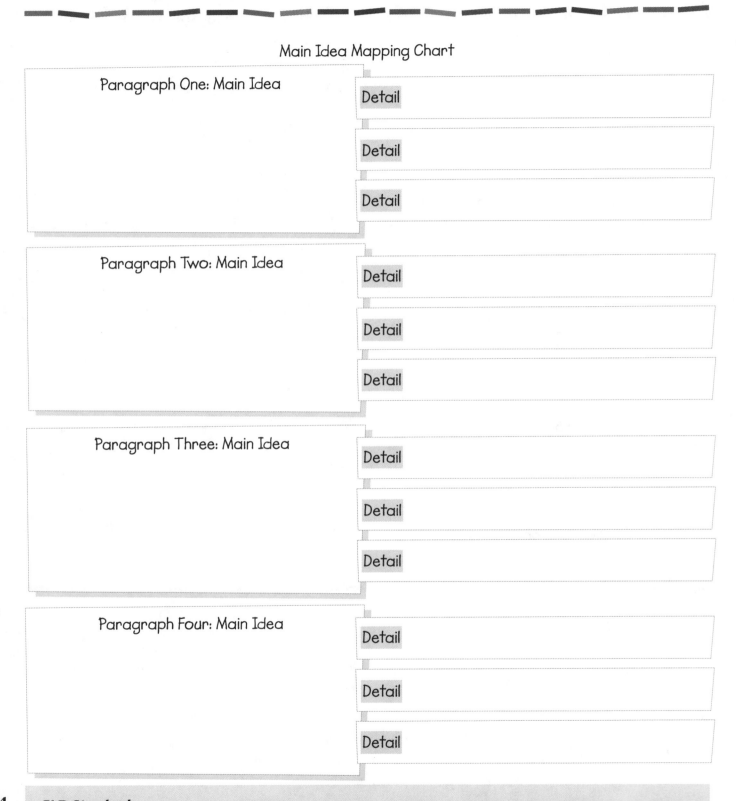

Paragraph One: Main Idea

Detail

Detail

Detail

Paragraph Two: Main Idea

Detail

Detail

Detail

Paragraph Three: Main Idea

Detail

Detail

Detail

Paragraph Four: Main Idea

Detail

Detail

Detail

ELD Standard
　Read and orally identify the main ideas and use them to draw inferences about written text using simple sentences.
ELA Standard
　Discuss main ideas and concepts presented in text identifying and assessing evidence that supports those ideas.

Name   Date

ⓐ Demonstrating Comprehension

- Read the poem *Columbus* to a partner.
- Read the poem again. Listen for the rhythm and rhyme in the poem.
- Read the poem *Columbus* again. Stop after each stanza.
  Your partner sums up what each stanza is mainly about.

Columbus by Joaquin Miller

Behind him lay the gray Azures.
  Behind the Gates of Hercules.
Before him not the ghost of shores.
  Before him only shoreless seas.
The good mate said: "Now must we pray.   5
  For lo! The very stars are gone.
Brave Adm'r'l speak; what shall I say?"
  "Why say: Sail on! Sail on and on!"

"My men grow mutinous day by day;
  My men grow ghastly wan and weak.   10
The stout mate thought of home: a spray
  Of salt washed his swarthy cheek.
"What shall I say, brave Adm'r'l say.
  If we sight naught but seas at dawn?"
"Why you shall say at break of day: 15
  Sail on! Sail on! Sail on and on."

They sailed and sailed, as winds might blow.
  Until at last the blanched mate said:
"Why, now not even God would know
  Should I and all my men fall dead.   20
These very winds forget their way.
  For God from these dread seas is gone.
Now speak brave Adm'r'l speak and say—"
  He said, "Sail on! Sail on! Sail on and on!"

ELD Standard
  Read and orally identify the main ideas and concepts presented in text, identifying and assessing evidence to support
  those ideas.
ELA Standard
  Discern main ideas and concepts in text, identifying and assessing evidence that support those ideas.

They sailed. They sailed. Then spake the mate: 25
   "This mad sea shows his teeth tonight.
He curls his lip, he lies in wait.
   With lifted teeth, as if to bite!
Brave Adm'r'l say but one good word:
   What shall we do when hope is gone?"   30
The words leapt like a leaping sword:
   "Sail on! Sail on! Sail on and on!"

Then pale and worn, he kept his deck.
   And peered through darkness. Ah, that night.
Of all dark nights! And then a speck —   35
   A light! A light! A light! A light!
It grew, a starlit flag unfurled!
   It grew to be Time's burst of dawn.
He gained a world: he gave that world
   Its grandest lesson: "On! Sail on!"   40

1. The speaker in this poem is probably a —
   - [ ] pilot
   - [ ] teacher
   - [ ] sailor or mate
   - [ ] carpenter

2. This poem is written to show —
   - [ ] Columbus' journey was an easy one
   - [ ] Columbus persisted to reach America
   - [ ] Columbus' mates were old
   - [ ] how the Native Americans sailed

3. What mood has the poet created in this poem?
   - [ ] merriment
   - [ ] despair
   - [ ] surprise
   - [ ] calmness

4. In the second stanza, the speaker describes how the men —
   - [ ] wash their clothes
   - [ ] grow wan and weak
   - [ ] like to sail
   - [ ] cook dinner on the ship

5. In line four of the first stanza, the word "shoreless" means —
   - [ ] sea
   - [ ] stuffed
   - [ ] without an admiral
   - [ ] without a shore

6. There is enough information in this poem to show that —
   - [ ] Columbus met the Native Americans when he saw lights
   - [ ] Columbus was a carpenter
   - [ ] Columbus had a difficult journey sailing across the sea
   - [ ] Columbus was not persistent

Name_____   Date_____

b Analyzing Poetry

▬ ▬ ▬ ▬ ▬ ▬ ▬ ▬ ▬ ▬ ▬ ▬ ▬ ▬ ▬ ▬ ▬ ▬

- Read the poem to a partner.
- Answer the questions below in complete sentences.

▬ ▬ ▬ ▬ ▬ ▬ ▬ ▬ ▬ ▬ ▬ ▬ ▬ ▬ ▬ ▬ ▬ ▬

1. Who is the brave Adm'r'l in the poem?

   _____

2. What is the main theme of the poem?

   _____

3. A *refrain* is a group of lines that is repeated in a poem. What refrain is repeated in this poem? What was the author's purpose for repeating this refrain after every stanza in the poem? Why is the refrain important to the meaning of the poem?

   _____

   _____

   _____

   _____

   _____

   _____

4. What are the rhyming words in the poem.

   _____

ELD Standard
   Independently write simple responses to literature.
ELA Standard
   Identify and analyze the characteristics of poetry, drama, fiction, and nonfiction, and explain the appropriateness of literary forms chosen by the author of a specific purpose.

5. Columbus faced many difficulties sailing to America. His shipmates got sick and there was little food. Make a mind map of all the challenges Columbus faced. In spite of the challenges, Columbus told his mates to "Sail on!" Write the challenges on the mind map and under each challenge write the refrain, "Sail on! Sail on!"

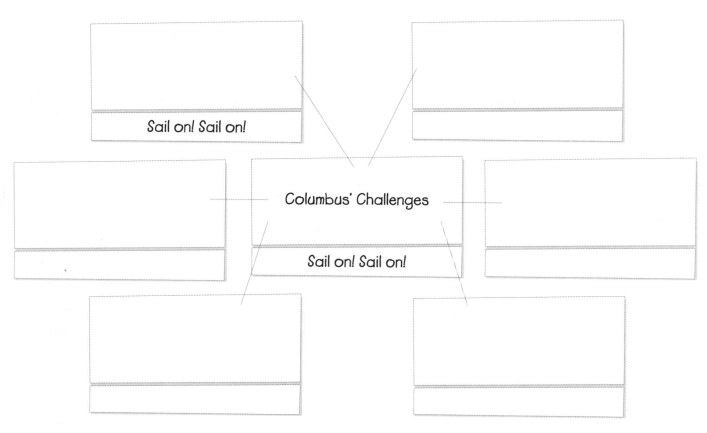

6. Describe how the expression "Perseverance you need to succeed" applied to Columbus in this poem.

_____

_____

7. Describe why the author wrote the poem.

_____

_____

8. What is the sea in lines 26 – 28 compared to?

_____

Name _____   Date _____

a Irregular Past Tense Verbs

■ Read the words on the chart below. The chart has irregular past tense verbs.

Irregular Verbs

✔ You do not always add *ed* to form the past tense of verbs. Verbs that *do not add ed* to make the past tense are called <u>irregular verbs</u>. You must learn these irregular verbs.

Verb	Past	Past with has, have or had
grow	grew	has, have *or* had grown
make	made	has, have *or* had made
build	built	has, have *or* had built
understand	understood	has, have *or* had understood
tell	told	has, have *or* had told
speak	spoke	has, have *or* had spoken
take	took	has, have *or* had taken
ride	rode	has, have *or* had ridden
do	did	has, have *or* had done
bend	bent	has, have *or* had bent

■ Write the underlined verb in the past tense.

■ Read the sentences to a partner.

1. Marcos (write) _____wrote_____ an essay on the Mayan civilization.

2. The Maya (live) _____ in Mexico and Guatemala more than 1500 years ago.

ELD Standard
    Use correct parts of speech.
ELA Standard
    Identify and use present, past, and future verb tenses in writing and speaking.

3. The Maya (make) _____ beautiful pottery, statues and jewelry.

4. People (speak) _____ of the wonderful civilization the Mayans built.

5. We haven't (understand) _____ anything the tour guide has said. He speaks too fast.

6. The Maya (grow) _____ and stored corn and were wonderful artists.

7. The Aztecs (build) _____ the great city of Tenochtitlan.

8. The Incas (take) _____ great blocks of stone and built homes and temples.

9. The Aztecs (bend) _____ and set broken bones.

10. The museum guide (tell) _____ us about three great American civilizations: the Mayas, the Incas and the Aztecs.

11. The Aztecs had (do) _____ many great things, such as build roads, canals and aqueducts.

12. The Maya (build) _____ more than forty cities with huge pyramid temples.

13. The Aztecs (settle) _____ in central Mexico.

14. My teacher has (speak) _____ about Machu Picchu, an ancient Inca city.

15. The Maya (understand) _____ mathematics and astronomy.

16. The Incas (build) _____ aqueducts to carry water from mountain streams to their crops.

17. The Incas (do) _____ study astronomy, indeed!

Name _____   Date _____

ⓐ Demonstrating Comprehension

- Read the passage to a partner. Your partner *sums up* the main idea for each paragraph.
- Answer the questions with a partner.

Establishing Missions in California

Santa Cruz

It was in the year 1765 that a man named Jose Galvez arrived on the shores of California. Jose was very ambitious. He wanted to gain the approval of the Spanish king. He decided one way to get the king to favor him was to establish new settlements in America for Spain. As he looked around California, he decided that California was the perfect place to set up a settlement.

After exploring California, Jose returned to Spain and spoke to the king. He told him that if the king supported him in his plan to set up a settlement in California, he would bring back riches for Spain. He also informed the king that, unless Spain settled California, Russia or England might take California for its own. The king decided to support Jose Galvez's plan to set up missions in California.

Galvez then <u>solicited</u> the help of a priest named Padre Junipero Serra. Galvez asked Padre Serra to start a chain of missions in California. Padre Serra agreed to establish the missions because he wanted to convert the Native Americans in California to Christianity. Galvez wasn't interested in converting the Native Americans. He was only interested in riches and glory, which he thought the establishment of the missions would bring him.

---

1. In this story, solicited means —
   - ☐ sold
   - ☐ asked
   - ☐ sent
   - ☐ took

2. In order to answer question one, the reader should —
   - ☐ reread the ending of the article
   - ☐ read the last line of each paragraph
   - ☐ look in the article for the word <u>solicited</u>
   - ☐ read the title

ELD Standard
Describe main ideas and supporting details of a text.
ELA Standard
Discern main ideas and concepts presented in texts identifying and assessing evidence that supports those ideas.

121

3. Another good title for this article is —
   - [ ] Establishing Mission Santa Cruz in 1791
   - [ ] Padre Junipero Serra
   - [ ] The Beginning of the Missions in Texas
   - [ ] Jose's Motives

4. There is enough information in this article to show that —
   - [ ] all the missions looked alike
   - [ ] Padre Serra and Jose Galvez were very smart. They wanted to set up missions in Oregon.
   - [ ] Jose Galvez lived in Italy
   - [ ] Jose Galvez and Padre Serra had different motives for wanting to establish the missions

5. Look at the map of the missions below. What might be a reason for the Spaniards to build Mission San Rafael Arcangel and San Francisco de Solano when they did?
   - [ ] They didn't want the Russians to move south. The Russians built Fort Ross.
   - [ ] Jose Galvez was interested in converting all Native Americans in California to Christianity.
   - [ ] Padre Junipero Serra was only interested in riches and glory.
   - [ ] The king of Spain wanted more people to colonize California.

6. Where were most of the missions built?
   - [ ] in the desert
   - [ ] in the mountains
   - [ ] along El Camino Real
   - [ ] on California's beaches

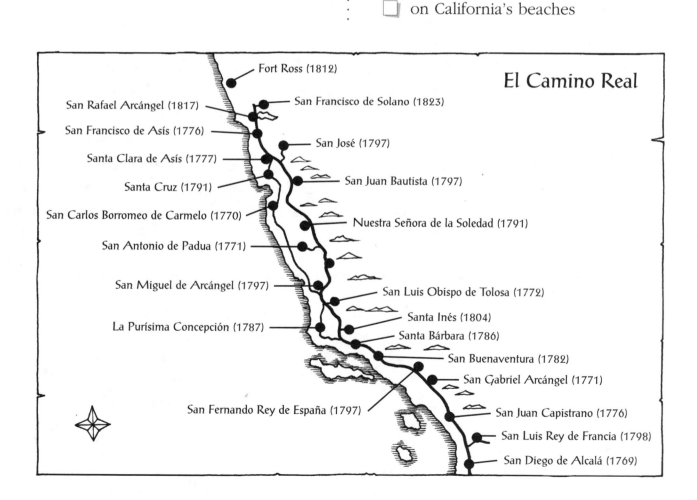

El Camino Real

Fort Ross (1812)
San Francisco de Solano (1823)
San Rafael Arcángel (1817)
San Francisco de Asís (1776)
Santa Clara de Asís (1777)
San José (1797)
Santa Cruz (1791)
San Juan Bautista (1797)
San Carlos Borromeo de Carmelo (1770)
Nuestra Señora de la Soledad (1791)
San Antonio de Padua (1771)
San Miguel de Arcángel (1797)
San Luis Obispo de Tolosa (1772)
Santa Inés (1804)
La Purísima Concepción (1787)
Santa Bárbara (1786)
San Buenaventura (1782)
San Gabriel Arcángel (1771)
San Fernando Rey de España (1797)
San Juan Capistrano (1776)
San Luis Rey de Francia (1798)
San Diego de Alcalá (1769)

Name _____   Date _____

b Informative Writing

Informative Writing

✔ Informative writing gives reasons for something.

It compares people or things and explains their difference and similarities.

Writing Prompt

■ Explain the motives of Jose Galvez for establishing the missions compared to those of Padre Serra.

Before Writing: Complete the Venn diagram comparing the motives of the two men on the two sides of the circle. Put how the men were alike in the middle. Think of colorful, descriptive words to present your facts.

After Writing: Use the writing checklist. Read your explanation to a partner.

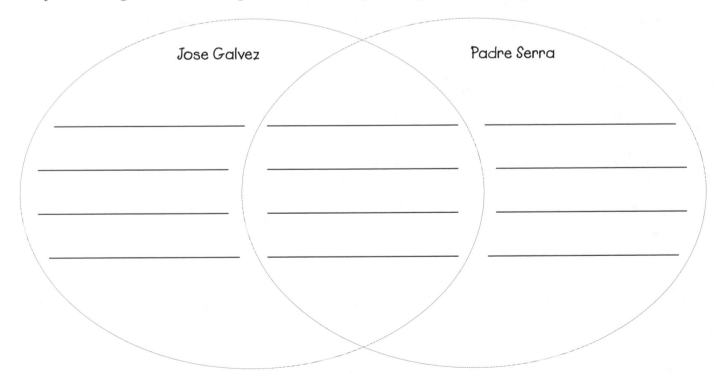

Jose Galvez   Padre Serra

■ On a separate sheet of paper, write a narrative about the story. Start your work by writing "The motives of."

ELD Standard
    Write a brief narrative.
ELA Standard
    Write responses to literature.

Name   Date

ⓐ Subject and Object Pronouns

✔ Using pronouns is a good way to avoid repeating a noun or a group of words containing a noun. There are subject pronouns and object pronouns.

Pronouns

✔ A <u>pronoun</u> is a word that takes the place of one or more nouns.

✔ <u>Subject pronouns</u> are *I, you, he, she, it, we* and *they.*

Pilgrims started the first colonies in New England.
They started the first colonies in New England.

✔ <u>Object pronouns</u> are *me, you, him, her, it, us* and *them.*

The pilgrims caught *fish.*
The pilgrims caught *them.*

▪ Replace each underlined word or group of words with a pronoun.

▪ Rewrite each sentence using the pronoun.

▪ Read the rewritten sentences to a partner.

1. <u>The Pilgrims</u> left England because they wanted religious freedom.

   _____

2. <u>The ship the Pilgrims sailed on</u> was called the *Mayflower.*

   _____

3. The Pilgrims learned how to grow crops, such as beans and corn, from <u>members of the Wampanoag nation</u>.

   _____

   _____

ELD Standard
   Use correct parts of speech including correct subject/verb agreement.
ELA Standard
   Identify and correctly use verbs that are often misused, modifiers, and pronouns.

4. Massasoit, the leader of the Wampanoag nation, was born in the village of Pokanoket around 1590. <u>Massasoit</u> changed his name to Woosamequen later in his life.

_____

_____

_____

5. The Mayflower Compact, a document forming a government, was signed by <u>41 pilgrims</u>.

_____

_____

6. <u>Mary Brewster</u> was one of the passengers on the *Mayflower*.

_____

7. <u>My brothers, sisters and I</u> are descendants of the pilgrims.

_____

8. Last year's Thanksgiving dinner was made by <u>my aunt</u>.

_____

9. People celebrate <u>Thanksgiving</u>, a holiday created to celebrate the Pilgrims survival, every November.

_____

_____

10. The Plimouth Colony was governed by <u>William Bradford</u> for 30 years.

_____

Name   Date

⬚ Using Colons

✔ A <u>colon</u> is used to set off a list or series.

Here are the names of the Southern colonies: Virginia, Maryland, North Carolina and Georgia.

✔ A <u>colon</u> is used to separate hours and minutes in time.

5:34

✔ A <u>colon</u> follows a greeting in a business letter.

Dear Mr. President:

■ Add a colon to make each sentence correct.

■ Read the sentences to a partner.

1. We are going to have a history test on the Southern colonies at 10 45.

2. The plantations in Jamestown grew four types of crops cotton, tobacco, peanuts and beans.

3. There were four Middle colonies Pennsylvania, New York and New Jersey.

4. I am going to begin the letter with *Dear Mr. President* and then close with *Yours Truly*.

5. The ship arrived at the port at 9 30.

6. The New England colonies were the following Massachusetts, New Hampshire, Rhode Island and Connecticut.

7. The colonists raised many animals goats, pigs, cows chickens and ducks.

8. The papers were delivered at 5 15.

9. The letter began with *To Whom It May Concern* and ended with *Sincerely*.

10. We are going to write an essay on three things farming, medicine and fun in the Southern colonies.

11. I am writing a letter that begins *Dear Senator* and goes on to congratulate him for his election victory.

ELD Standard
    Edit writing for basic conventions (e.g., punctuation, capitalization, and spelling).
ELA Standard
    Use a colon to separate hours and minutes and to introduce a list.

Name _____   Date _____

ⓐ Demorating Comprehension

▬▬ ▬ ▬ ▬▬ ▬ ▬ ▬ ▬▬ ▬ ▬ ▬ ▬▬ ▬ ▬ ▬ ▬▬ ▬ ▬

Reminder

✔ A **fact** is a sentence that is true. *A dog has four legs.*

✔ An **opinion** is what someone thinks or feels. *My dog Rex is the smartest dog on my block.*

▬▬ ▬ ▬ ▬▬ ▬ ▬ ▬ ▬▬ ▬ ▬ ▬ ▬▬ ▬ ▬ ▬ ▬▬ ▬ ▬

■ Read the questions on page 128.

■ Read the passage below to a partner. Your partner *sums up* the main idea after each paragraph.

■ Answer the questions. Discuss your answers with a partner.

■ Write a summary of this passage on a separate sheet of paper.

Pennsylvania

Pennsylvania is the best of England's colonies in America.

(1) Pennsylvania is one of the Middle colonies. King Charles II of England granted the land for the colony to William Penn in 1681 as payment of debt owed to his father, Admiral Sir William Penn. William Penn named the colony "Pennsylvania" in honor of his father. Pennsylvania is another way of saying "Penn's Woods." "Sylvania" comes from the Latin "silvanus" referring to forest or woods.

(2) William Penn wanted people to move to Pennsylvania so he wrote letters advertising life in Pennsylvania. William Penn tried to convince people to come to live in Pennsylvania. William told people Pennsylvania was a great place to live. There was land for farming with water for the crops. Penn said people could start a new life in Pennsylvania and live without religious persecution.

(3) Penn nicknamed Pennsylvania "The Quaker State." Penn had been persecuted in England as a Quaker. He was determined that Pennsylvania should be a place where people of all faiths would have religious freedom.

ELD Standard
    Read and orally identify examples of fact/opinion and cause/effect in literature and content area texts.
ELA Standard
    Distinguish facts, supported inferences and opinions in text.

(4) Thousands and thousands of Europeans sailed to North America and settled in Pennsylvania. Many people came to Pennsylvania after reading William Penn's advertisements. They came to Pennsylvania to start farms and to pursue their religious beliefs.

1. Which of these is an *opinion* in this article?
   - ☐ Pennsylvania is another way of saying "Penn's Woods."
   - ☐ Admiral Penn was William Penn's father.
   - ☐ Pennsylvania is one of England's middle colonies.
   - ☐ Pennsylvania is the best of England's colonies in America.

2. What is the nickname of Pennsylvania?
   - ☐ The Long State
   - ☐ The Penn State
   - ☐ The Farm State
   - ☐ The Quaker State

3. If the author added a sentence to the end of paragraph 1, which of these would fit best?
   - ☐ William Penn was proud to be able to honor his father.
   - ☐ Pennsylvania was a Quaker state.
   - ☐ William Penn himself was persecuted in England as a Quaker, so religious freedom was important to him.
   - ☐ Thousands of people traveled to Pennsylvania.

4. The author included paragraph 2 in order to —
   - ☐ tell how William Penn wrote letters to convince people to move to Pennsylvania
   - ☐ tell about Pennsylvania's nickname
   - ☐ describe a farm in Pennsylvania
   - ☐ describe the lives of William Penn and other Quakers who went to Pennsylvania

5. In order to answer question 4, the best thing to do is —
   - ☐ skim the whole article
   - ☐ reread the first sentence of each paragraph
   - ☐ think about a title for the third paragraph
   - ☐ reread the second paragraph

6. Another good title for this article is —
   - ☐ Admiral Penn
   - ☐ A Long Journey
   - ☐ Come Settle in Pennsylvania
   - ☐ The Last Colony

Name _____   Date _____

b Writing a Persuasive Letter

✔ A letter has a salutation (Dear _____), the date, a body and a closing (Your Friend).

✔ A persuasive letter is written to convince someone to do something.
  Facts are used to persuade someone to do something.

Writing Prompt

▪ On a separate sheet of paper, write a letter to the citizens of England from William Penn inviting them to move to the colony of Pennsylvania.

  Before Writing: Make a mind map to list reasons for people to take a ship to the colony of Pennsylvania.

  After Writing: Use the writing checklist to edit your work.
           Read your letter to a partner.

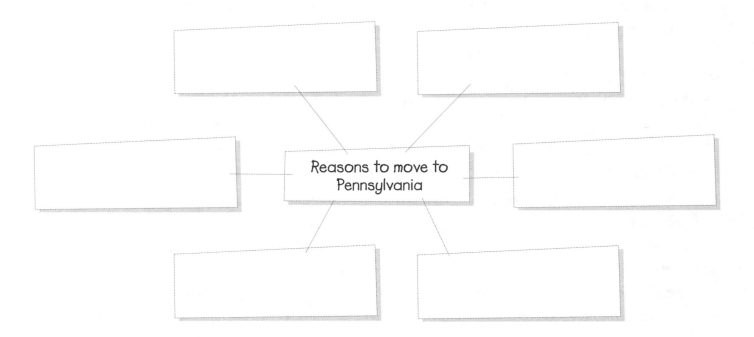

ELD Standard
   Independently write a persuasive letter with relevant information.
ELA Standard
   Write persuasive letters or compositions. Support a position with relevant information.

129

Name   Date

a Demonstrating Comprehension

✔ Sometimes the answers are not written in a story.

✔ In these cases, we have to *infer*, or draw a conclusion, after we see the facts.

Facts:

[1] The colonists had to pay more taxes to King George III.

[2] The colonists had no representation in the English parliament.

[3] The colonists had to house British troops and feed them without receiving payment.

We can infer that the colonists were treated unfairly.

■ Read the questions on page 131 first. Read the passage to a partner.

■ Your partner sums up the main idea. Answer the questions.

Independence for the American Colonies

The American colonies had been part of Great Britain for a long time. They looked upon George III as their king. But now the king was doing things that were making the colonists angry. The king said they could not move farther to the west into the land of the Native Americans and that the colonists had to pay more taxes. In 1776, a group of patriots decided to break away from Great Britain. On July 4, 1776, the Declaration of Independence was signed. It said that the United States of America was a separate nation. This led to the Revolutionary War. George Washington, who later became the first president of the United States, was the leader of the American army. The war lasted for eight years. The British army surrendered in 1781 and, in 1783, Great Britain agreed that the colonies were now free and independent. America was now a free country.

Now that America was independent, Americans had to decide what kind of government to have. Americans did not want a government like Britain with its king and parliament. The thirteen colonies were now states. Each state had its own constitution, or written set of laws. The first national government was very weak – weaker than the government of each state. People knew they had to make the national government stronger. A group of delegates, or representatives, met in Philadelphia and talked and argued all summer. The meeting was called the Constitutional Convention. In the end, they wrote a document that gave the government the power to call for an army and collect taxes among other things. The first ten ammendments are called The Bill of Rights.

1. If you wanted to know more about the Declaration of Independence, you should —
   - ☐ go to the capitol building in California
   - ☐ read a science book
   - ☐ study a history book
   - ☐ study a United States map

2. This article was mainly written in order to —
   - ☐ explain the Constitution
   - ☐ describe George Washington
   - ☐ tell you about two famous people
   - ☐ give you a history lesson

3. What is the second paragraph mainly about?
   - ☐ the writing of the U.S. Constitution
   - ☐ George Washington's army
   - ☐ the Declaration of Independence
   - ☐ King George III

4. Another good title for this article is —
   - ☐ The Fourth of July
   - ☐ America and Asia
   - ☐ America Becomes a Separate Nation
   - ☐ America's Flag

5. What can you infer from this article?
   - ☐ The American colonies wanted to be a part of France or Spain.
   - ☐ The American colonists looked upon King George III as their king.
   - ☐ Great Britain agreed that its American colonies were now free and independent.
   - ☐ The colonists agreed that 13 divided states can be conquered more easily than one united country.

6. Here are some important ideas from this article. Which of these belongs in the empty box?
   - ☐ George Washington
   - ☐ Declaration of Independence
   - ☐ 13 Colonies
   - ☐ Great Britain

The American Colonies

Constitution

Made the U.S. a separate nation

Led to the Revolutionary War

Gave the government the power to collect taxes

Gave the government the power to call for an army

ELD Standard
Read and orally identify the main ideas and use them to draw inferences about written text using simple sentences.
ELA Standard
Discern main ideas and concepts presented in texts, identifying and assessing evidence that support those ideas.

Name _____   Date _____

ⓐ Demonstrating Comprehension

■ Read the questions on page 133 first.

■ Read the passage to a partner. Your partner *sums up* the main idea after each paragraph.

■ Answer the questions.

National Symbols

(1) What would you think if a wild turkey were our national symbol? Over 200 years ago, Benjamin Franklin suggested that the turkey be chosen for the United States' symbol. Franklin didn't like the eagle much. He thought that the turkey was a wise and clever bird. He also knew that it played a role in the history of our nation. The wild turkey was an important food for early settlers.

The Great Seal of the United States

(2) Other people thought the eagle was a better symbol for the freedom and power of our nation. The bald eagle has great strength. With its huge wings, it flies high and free above the land. An eagle's eyes can see movement below from hundreds of feet in the air. For all these reasons, the bald eagle became our national symbol. Different nations use different symbols to show their feelings about themselves and their land. Americans pick national symbols that stand for what is special about our country. Our symbols stand for our pride and good feelings about the United States.

(3) For example, the Liberty Bell is a symbol of the liberty, or freedom, that Americans believe in. The Liberty Bell was rung in 1776 when the United States declared its independence from England. Today it hangs in Philadelphia, Pennsylvania.

(4) Other cities have monuments that are national symbols. A monument is a building that honors a person or an event. If you were to visit our nation's capital, Washington, D.C., you could see the tall Washington Monument. It was built to honor George Washington. The Gateway Arch stands west of the Mississippi River in St. Louis, Missouri. This stainless steel monument honors the pioneers who moved west to settle the land.

ELD Standard
  Describe main ideas and supporting details in text.
ELA Standard
  Discuss main ideas and concepts presented in texts, identifying and assessing evidence that support those ideas.

(5) These symbols are special because they remind us of important ideas and beliefs about our country and our land. That is why we should try to preserve them. Today the bald eagle is so rare that it is in danger of dying out. Pollution and hunting have put the bald eagle in danger. Changes to the land have made it hard for the eagle to find food and locate places for nests. It is important to preserve the bald eagle because it is one of our nation's symbols.

---

1. In this story, <u>a symbol</u> means —
   - [ ] something that stands for what is special about our country
   - [ ] buildings that are built in the Philadelphia, Washington D.C., and St. Louis.
   - [ ] turkeys that are wise and clever
   - [ ] important foods eaten by early settlers

2. People use national symbols to —
   - [ ] stop pollution
   - [ ] show the strength of the eagle
   - [ ] tell the difference between monuments
   - [ ] show their pride and good feelings about themselves and their land

3. What is the monument used for?
   - [ ] to stand for a state
   - [ ] to honor a person or event
   - [ ] to preserve the eagle
   - [ ] to preserve coins

4. The second paragraph explains —
   - [ ] why coins were used in the U.S.
   - [ ] why the eagle was chosen as a symbol
   - [ ] why the turkey was chosen as a symbol
   - [ ] why Benjamin Franklin needed money

5. This article is mainly about —
   - [ ] Benjamin Franklin
   - [ ] the history of our nation
   - [ ] national symbols
   - [ ] turkeys and eagles

6. This article is most like —
   - [ ] an adventure story
   - [ ] a biography
   - [ ] a history lesson
   - [ ] a folktale

7. Another good title for this article is —
   - [ ] The Endangered Species
   - [ ] Famous Cities
   - [ ] United States Symbols
   - [ ] The Liberty Bell

8. What can you infer from this article?
   - [ ] Different nations use different symbols to show their feelings about themselves and their land.
   - [ ] The Gateway Arch in St. Louis, Missouri honors the pioneers who moved west to settle the land.
   - [ ] People probably selected the eagle over the turkey because the eagle is more elegant and powerful.
   - [ ] The United States would have no symbols if it didn't declare independence from Great Britain.

Name   Date

ⓑ Persuasive Writing

Persuasive Writing

✔ Persuasive writing convinces someone to do something.

It convinces someone to accept your point of view.

Writing Prompt

■ Create a symbol to represent your school.

On a separate sheet of paper, write at least three paragraphs to convince your classmates that the symbol you created is the best symbol for your school.

Before Writing: Think of the meaning you want to convey with the symbol.

Think of how the symbol represents your school.

Draw the symbol.

After Writing: Use the writing checklist at the back of the book.

Have a partner use the writing checklist to edit your work.

Read your paragraph to a partner.

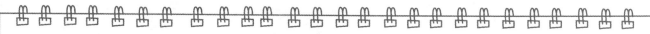

Your school symbol

ELD Standard

Independently write a persuasive letter or essay with relevant information.

ELA Standard

Write persuasive letters or compositions. Support a position with relevant information.

Name _____   Date _____

ⓐ Interpreting Charts

The three branches of the United States Government

Legislative Branch	**Executive Branch**	**Judicial Branch**
"We make, or enact, the laws."	*"We protect the Constitution. We settle cases on our nation's laws."*	*"We protect the Constitution. We settle cases on our nation's laws."*
House & Senate	**President & Vice President**	**Supreme Court**

Secretary of State
"I deal with foreign countries."

Secretary of Treasury
"I raise money and plan spending."

Department of Justice
"I am the Attorney General. I protect our citizens and enforce our laws."

Secretary of Veteran Affairs
"I help veterans and their families."

Secretary of Interior
"I plan the use of land and water."

Secretary of Health and Human Services
"I help protect the health of all Americans."

Executive Branch

President & Vice President

Secretary of Commerce
"I help business."

Secretary of Transportation
"I look after the country's transportation system."

Secretary of Labor
"I help workers."

Secretary of Agriculture
"I oversee all agriculture."

Secretary of Housing and Urban Affairs
"I plan policies for housing."

Secretary of Education
"I establish policy for our nation's schools."

Secretary of Energy
"I help our nation maintain its energy needs."

Secretary of Defense
"I look after our defense."

ELD Standard
    Read and identify text features, such as titles, tables of contents, chapter headings, diagrams, and charts.
ELA Standard
    Understand how text features (e.g., format, graphics, sequence, diagrams, illustrations, charts, maps) make information accessible and usable.

■ Read the chart on page 135 to a partner.
  Discuss the functions of different members of the government.

■ Answer the questions in complete sentences.

1. Which branch of government settles cases about the country's laws?

   _____

2. The President presides over which branch of government?

   _____

3. What is the function of the legislative branch of government?

   _____

4. What is the job of the Secretary of Treasury?

   _____

5. What is the job of the Secretary of State?

   _____

6. Write a sentence telling what the Secretary of Agriculture does.

   _____

7. Write a sentence telling what the Secretary of Transportation does.

   _____

8. Who looks after the Department of Justice?

   _____

Name _____   Date _____

ⓐ Demonstrating Comprehension

- -

The Western Frontier
Why did Americans Continue to Explore the West?

There were many reasons why Americans continued to explore the western frontier in the last part of the nineteenth century. Gold was discovered in California in 1849 and silver was discovered in Nevada ten years later. This prompted miners and their families to move west. The Homestead Act of 1862 promised people 160 acres of prairie land if they promised to stay and farm the land for five years. Farmers who agreed were called <u>homesteaders</u>. A transcontinental railroad was built which made it easier to make the journey west.

After Americans explored the West, many people were content to improve America's cities and farmlands and keep to themselves. But some explorers, politicians and business people were still looking for new opportunities. In 1867, Secretary of State William Seward arranged for the government to buy Alaska from Russia. Soon, America had control over lands throughout the world including Hawaii, Puerto Rico, Samoa, the Midway Islands, the Philippines and Guam. Some people thought it was wrong for America to want colonies or to become involved in another country's politics. These people were known as *isolationists*. Others, known as *imperialists*, believed it was America's duty to expand throughout the world. They also believed it was important for American businesses to own islands to use as refueling stations for trade ships. Another way America improved its ability to trade was to buy the rights to land in Panama, where America built the Panama Canal in 1914.

ELD Standard
    Read and use detailed sentences to orally identify main ideas and use them to make predictions and provide supporting details for predictions made.
ELA Standard
    Draw inferences, conclusions or generalizations about text and support them with textual evidence and prior knowledge.

137

1. Silver was discovered in —
   - [ ] California
   - [ ] Florida
   - [ ] Nevada
   - [ ] Texas

2. The Homestead Act of 1862 promised people —
   - [ ] a journey west
   - [ ] a new home and horses
   - [ ] 120 acres of land
   - [ ] 160 acres of land

3. In this article, <u>isolationists</u> means —
   - [ ] the islands in the Philippines
   - [ ] refueling stations
   - [ ] people who believed America should expand throughout the world
   - [ ] people who thought it was wrong for America to become involved in other country's politics

4. This article was written mainly to —
   - [ ] tell about discovering gold
   - [ ] tell about homesteaders
   - [ ] tell about exploring the western frontier in America
   - [ ] tell about the isolationists

5. This article is most like —
   - [ ] a true story
   - [ ] an adventure story
   - [ ] a history lesson
   - [ ] a folktale

6. The Panama Canal was built in —
   - [ ] 1812
   - [ ] 1849
   - [ ] 1867
   - [ ] 1914

7. Silver was discovered in Nevada in —
   - [ ] 1839
   - [ ] 1849
   - [ ] 1859
   - [ ] 1869

8. What would an imperialist say?
   - [ ] "The United States should not expand its territory."
   - [ ] "The United States should not become involved in other countries' affairs."
   - [ ] "American businesses need other countries' resources."
   - [ ] "American companies should do business in the United States only."

Name   Date

b Writing a Summary

Writing Prompt

- Write a summary of this article on a separate sheet of paper.

    Before Writing: List the main ideas and important details in each paragraph.

    After Writing: Use the writing checklist at the back of the book.
                        Read your summary to a partner.

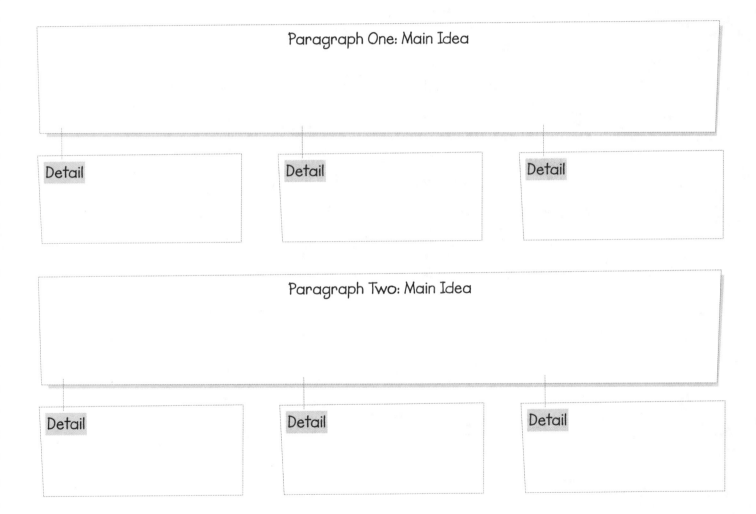

Paragraph One: Main Idea

Detail   Detail   Detail

Paragraph Two: Main Idea

Detail   Detail   Detail

ELD Standard
    Write a brief narrative.
ELA Standard
    Write narratives. Show, rather than tell, the events of a story.

Name _____   Date _____

a Irregular Past Tense Verbs

▬ ▬ ▬ ▬ ▬ ▬ ▬ ▬ ▬ ▬ ▬ ▬ ▬ ▬ ▬ ▬ ▬ ▬

■ Read the irregular past tense verbs on the chart.

▬ ▬ ▬ ▬ ▬ ▬ ▬ ▬ ▬ ▬ ▬ ▬ ▬ ▬ ▬ ▬ ▬ ▬

Irregular Verbs

✔ You do not always add _ed_ to form the past tense of verbs. Verbs that do not add _ed_ to make the past tense are called irregular verbs. You must learn these irregular verbs.

Verb	Past	Past with has, have or had
build	built	has, have or had built
make	made	has, have or had made
bring	brought	has, have or had brought
am, is, are	was, were	has, have or had been
beseech	besought	has, have or had besought
bid	bade	has, have or had bade
blow	blew	has, have or had blown
choose	chose	has, have or had chosen
do	bid	has, have or had done
grow	grew	has, have or had grown

140

ELD Standard
   Use correct parts of speech.
ELA Standard
   Identify and use present, past, and future tenses in writing and speaking.

Write the verb in parentheses in the past tense. Read the sentences to a partner.

1. The Industrial Revolution (bring) _____ about many new inventions.

2. The whistle of the train (blow) _____ when it came into a railroad station.

3. People (build) _____ many roads, canals and railroads.

4. Peter Cooper (is) _____ the inventor of the steam-powered locomotive.

5. American factories had (grow) _____ into large industries.

6. The steam-powered locomotive (make) _____ land travel faster.

7. Americans (do) _____ not agree on the policies for treating workers.

8. American engineer Robert Fulton (beseech) _____ business people to invest in his invention, the steamboat.

9. The man (bid) _____ his horse good-bye and traveled across country on the train.

10. The businesses in the North and South (choose) _____ different trade policies.

Name   Date

a Contractions

Contractions

✔ A contraction is a shortened and combined form of two words that uses an apostrophe to replace one or more letters.

does not ⟶ doesn't
is not ⟶ isn't

Two Words	Contraction
was not	wasn't
were not	weren't
did not	didn't
could not	couldn't
would not	wouldn't
had not	hadn't
have not	haven't
has not	hasn't

▪ Read each sentence. Write a contraction for the underlined words. Rewrite each sentence using the contraction.

▪ Read the sentences with contractions to a partner.

1. Some people in the South believed they <u>could not</u> live without slaves.

_____

2. People in the Northern states <u>did not</u> believe that anyone should use slaves for labor.

_____

3. Slaves from the South <u>were not</u> happy. They wanted their freedom.

_____

ELD Standard
   Spell correctly roots, inflections, suffixes and prefixes and syllable constructions.
ELA Standard
   Spell roots, suffixes, prefixes, contractions and syllable constructions correctly.

4. The people in the South <u>would not</u> agree to abolish slavery.

_____

5. Our class <u>has not</u> studied the effects of the Missouri Compromise.

_____

6. The Civil War started because the North and the South <u>could not</u> agree.

_____

7. The people who opposed slavery <u>did not</u> want it to exist anywhere in the United States.

_____

8. The underground railroad <u>was not</u> a real railroad.

_____

9. In 1856, the U.S. Supreme Court <u>had not</u> made its decision on the Dred Scott case.

_____

✔ We use contractions to ask yes/no questions.

Didn't slaves escape to freedom in Canada, Cuba, the Bahamas, or Mexico?

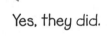

Yes, they did.

■ Ask and answer the questions with a partner.

1. Weren't there laws against slavery?

2. Wasn't the Civil War between the North and the South?

3. Didn't people protest slavery?

4. Couldn't people see that slavery was morally wrong?

5. Hadn't abolitionists chosen freedom over slavery?

Name   Date

ⓐ Demonstrating Comprehension

- Read the passage to a partner. Your partner sums up the main idea after each paragraph. Switch roles.

- Complete the main idea map for Lincoln's Gettysburg Address on page 146.

- Write a summary on a separate sheet of paper. Read your summary to a partner.

Lincoln's Gettysburg Address

Gettysburg

At 1:00 p.m. on July 3, 1863, the battle of Gettysburg started between the Confederate army from the southern states and the Union army from the northern states. One hundred and seventy cannons concentrated their fire on the clump of trees that marked the center of the Union army line. The storm of shot and shell dismembered horses, blew up ammunition wagons and cut men in half.

It took months to clean up the debris of battle after the fight at Gettysburg. The Union army's dead soldiers were collected from their temporary graves and moved to a new site atop Cemetery Hill. The Union Cemetery was to be dedicated on November 19, 1863. President Abraham Lincoln was asked to attend. He wasn't the main speaker. A distinguished orator, Edward Everett, was to give the speech. Lincoln was to say only a few remarks.

There was a crowd of 6,000 people. Everett spoke for an hour and 57 minutes. Lincoln spoke for only two minutes. However, Everett's speech was not to go down in history as significant. It was Lincoln's two-minute speech that became famous and immortalized the Gettysburg battle and the purpose of all the lives lost. This is what Lincoln said in his famous Gettysburg Address:

ELD Standard
    Read and orally identify the main ideas and use them to draw inferences about written text using simple sentences.
ELA Standard
    Discern main ideas and concepts presented in texts, identifying and assessing evidence that support those ideas.
    Understand that theme refers to the meaning or moral of a selection and recognize themes in sample works.

Four score and seven years ago our fathers brought forth on this continent, a new nation, conceived in liberty, and dedicated to the proposition that all men are created equal.

Now we are engaged in a great civil war, testing whether that nation, or any nation so conceived and so dedicated, can long endure. We are met on a great battlefield of that war. We have come to dedicate a portion of that field, as a final resting place for those who here gave their lives that that nation might live. It is altogether fitting and proper that we should do this.

But in a larger sense, we can not dedicate—we can not consecrate—we can not hallow—this ground. The brave men, living and dead, who struggled here, have consecrated it, far above our poor power to add or detract. The world will little note, nor long remember what we say here, but it can never forget what they did here. It is for us the living, rather, to be dedicated here to the unfinished work which they who fought here have thus far so nobly advanced. It is rather for us to be here dedicated to the great task remaining before us—that from these honored dead we take increased devotion to that cause for which they gave the last full measure of devotion—that we here highly resolve that these dead shall not have died in vain—that this nation, under God shall have a new birth of freedom—and that government of the people, by the people, for the people shall not perish from the earth.

Lincoln's two-minute speech was not applauded by anyone. Lincoln thought the speech was a failure. Yet, Lincoln's Gettysburg Address became one of the most important and significant speeches ever made.

Word Prompt

- On a separate sheet of paper, write a summary of this article including the main ideas and significant details in Lincoln's Gettysburg Address.

Before Writing: Complete the main idea mapping chart on page 146.

After Writing: Use the writing checklist at the back of the book.
Have a partner use the writing checklist to edit your writing.
Read your summary to a partner.

Main Idea Mapping Chart

Paragraph One: Main Idea	
	Detail
	Detail
	Detail

Paragraph Two: Main Idea	
	Detail
	Detail
	Detail

Paragraph Three: Main Idea	
	Detail
	Detail
	Detail

Paragraph Four: Main Idea	
	Detail
	Detail
	Detail

Name _____   Date _____

a Prepositions

Prepositions

✔ A <u>preposition</u> relates a noun or pronoun to another word in a sentence.

in the house   *near* the table   *with* the boy

✔ Prepositions have many purposes. For example, <u>prepositional phrases</u> sometimes tell us about time, place, movement, or purpose.

Time: The Homesteaders farmed the land <u>for five years</u>.

Place: Silver was discovered <u>in Nevada</u>.

Movement: The U.S. government made many Native Americans move <u>to reservations</u>.

Purpose: Cowboys used rope <u>for catching cattle</u>.

✔ Here is a list of some common prepositions:

above	across	over
to	under	with
after	around	at
behind	down	for
from	in	near
of	on	

▪ Read each sentence. Underline the preposition.

▪ Read the sentences to a partner.

1. Gold and silver were discovered in Nevada.

2. The miners and their families moved to the West.

3. Farmers put their crops behind the barn.

4. The transcontinental railroad went across the country.

5. Native Americans used buffalo for food and clothing.

ELD Standard
    Use correct parts of speech.
ELA Standard
    Identify and correctly use prepositional phrases, appositives and independent and dependent clauses; use transitions and conjunctions to connect ideas.

■ Complete each sentence by writing a preposition on the line.

■ Read the sentences to a partner.

1. The transcontinental railroad traveled from Oklahoma _____ Nevada.

2. Native Americans used buffalo skins _____ shelter.

3. The Homestead Act promised land _____ people who agreed to farm the land for five years.

4. Gold was discovered _____ California in 1849.

5. The Nevada mountains rose _____ the town.

■ Write one sentence for each of the following prepositions: after, of, near, around, on.

1. _____

2. _____

3. _____

4. _____

5. _____

Name _____   Date _____

a Singular and Plural Object Pronouns

✔ A <u>pronoun</u> is a word that takes the place of one or more nouns.

The singular object pronouns are *me, you, her, him* and *it*.

The plural object pronouns are *us, you* and *them*.

✔ Use object pronouns after action verbs and after <u>prepositions</u> such as *for, at, to in* or *with*.

▓ Underline the object pronoun in parentheses that correctly completes the sentence.

▓ Indicate whether the object pronoun is singular or plural.

▓ Read the sentences to a partner.

	Singular or Plural
Example: *It was clear to (<u>us</u>, we) that there were many machines at the end of the 1800s.*	plural
1. The machines improved life for (us, we).	_____
2. Edison invented the light bulb for me and (you, I).	_____
3. Railroads transported (they, them) across the country.	_____
4. The telephone enabled (he, him) to communicate with friends.	_____
5. The airplane was invented by two brothers. Wilbur and Orville Wright invented (it, they).	_____
6. The Machine Age changed life for all of (we, us).	_____
7. The electric light bulb allowed (she, her) to read at night.	_____
8. Where did you say the train was taking (they, them)?	_____

ELD Standard
    Use correct parts of speech including subject/verb agreement.
ELA Standard
    Identify and correctly use verbs that are often misused (e.g., lie/lay), modifiers, and pronouns.

149

■ Write a sentence using the object pronoun in parentheses.

■ Read your sentences to a partner.

1. (him) _____

_____

2. (them) _____

_____

3. (me) _____

_____

4. (us) _____

_____

5. (her) _____

_____

6. (you) _____

_____

7. (it) _____

_____

Name _____   Date _____

a Interpreting Poetry

✔ When we read something, we look at what the author wants to say. In poetry, we can also look at specific elements, such as *rhyme*, *rhythm*, and *refrain*.

Rhyme: Pairs of words with identical sounds, like *nice* and *mice*.

Rhythm: Patterns of stressed and unstressed syllables.

Refrain: Groups of words that are repeated.

Poems do not necessarily need to have all of these elements.
For example, some poems do not have rhymes.

■ Read the poem to a partner.

■ Read the poem again. Your partner sums up the meaning of each stanza.

■ Answer the questions.

■ Discuss the answers with a partner.

Immigration

America is a country
of immigrants, so they say.
Our ancestors all came
from countries far away.

Our European ancestors came   (5)
across the pond without much fame.
They came from Spain, Finland, Russia and Italy.
They came to America across the sea.
Many passed through Ellis Island, then
settled in New York and found,   (10)
many of their countrymen
when they looked around.

ELD Standard
    Apply knowledge of language to derive meaning/comprehension from literary texts.
ELA Standard
    Demonstrate an understanding of literary works. Identify and analyze the characteristics of poetry.

Our Asian ancestors came,
But it was not the same.
They had a long journey, it is true.   (15)
They traveled across the ocean blue.
Many came to San Francisco.
They established Chinatown.
They contributed a new culture and cuisine,
a boon to the American scene.   (20)

Our African ancestors came.
The economic system was partly to blame.
They were forced to come to America.
They brought their music, food, and toil
to work the American soil   (25)
and worked their inventions on the American shore.
Finally as free American citizens, they kept on contributing more.

Many of our ancestors came to America from Mexico.
They came to work, you know.
They came to help America's economy grow.   (30)
They brought their food,
music and culture too.
They came to become
Americans like me and you.

America is a country   (35)
of immigrants, so they say.
Our ancestors all came
from countries far away.

1. The speaker in this poem is probably —
   - [ ] a bear
   - [ ] a baby
   - [ ] a doctor
   - [ ] an immigrant

2. This poem was written to show —
   - [ ] how people immigrated to America
   - [ ] how to sail a ship
   - [ ] how to cook spaghetti
   - [ ] how people flew across the country

3. What mood has the poet created in this poem?
   - [ ] sadness
   - [ ] pride
   - [ ] silliness
   - [ ] slowness

4. In line two of the first stanza, the word "immigrants" means —
   - [ ] people who eat different foods
   - [ ] people who come into a country from another country
   - [ ] sailors
   - [ ] people who sail across an ocean

5. In the second stanza, the speaker describes —
   - [ ] how Mexicans came to America
   - [ ] how Africans came to America
   - [ ] how Europeans came to America
   - [ ] how Asians came to America

6. There is enough information in this poem to show that —
   - [ ] immigrants came to America only from Asia
   - [ ] immigrants came to America only from Africa
   - [ ] immigrants came to America only from Europe
   - [ ] immigrants came to America from many countries

7. On line six, the word <u>pond</u> refers to —
   - [ ] a small lake
   - [ ] Lake Michigan
   - [ ] the Pacific Ocean
   - [ ] the Atlantic Ocean

8. What is an example of a refrain?
   - [ ] lines 1–4 and 35-38
   - [ ] lines 5–12 and 13-20
   - [ ] lines 5, 13, and 21
   - [ ] lines 6, 14, 22, and 29

Name   Date

a Appositives

✔ An <u>appositive</u> follows a noun or pronoun to <u>explain</u> or <u>identify</u> the noun or pronoun.

Mrs. Brown, <u>my aunt</u>, lived on a farm.
<u>*My aunt*</u> is an appositive. It <u>identifies</u> Mrs. Brown.

Deer Creek, <u>a stream</u>, runs across the state.
<u>*A stream*</u> is an appositive. It <u>explains</u> what Deer Creek is.

✔ <u>An explanatory word or phrase that follows a noun or pronoun is an appositive</u>.
There are usually commas around an appositive.

▪ Underline the appositives in these sentences.

▪ Read the sentences to a partner.

1. My great grandfather, a farmer, explored the west during the 1800s.

2. America, a growing power, owned colonies throughout the world.

3. The Admiral, my grandfather, steered the ship through the Panama Canal.

4. Cuba, an island nation in the Caribbean, used to be a Spanish colony.

5. In 1893, the American minister to Hawaii, John L. Stevens, wanted the U.S. to annex the independent archipelago.

6. Imperialists, people who believed it was America's duty to expand around the world, wanted the Philippines to become a U.S. territory.

7. People who thought it was wrong for Americans to own colonies, *isolationists*, did not want the U.S. to expand its territory.

8. In 1867, Secretary of State William Seward arranged for the U.S. government to buy Alaska, a Russian colony, for $7.2 million.

9. Puerto Rico, a self-governing U.S. commonwealth, is in the Caribbean.

10. John, a diplomat, was involved in the country's politics.

11. Anthony, a politician, campaigned to become governor.

12. Mary, my mother, told me stories about Russia.

13. Theodore Roosevelt, President of the United States from 1901 to 1909, helped influence American policy at home and abroad.

ELD Standard
Use correct parts of speech including subject/verb agreement.
ELA Standard
Identify and correctly use prepositional phrases, appositives and independent and dependent clauses.

Name   Date

ⓐ Demonstrating Comprehension

- Read the questions first.
- Read the passage to a partner. Your partner sums up the main idea after each paragraph.
- Answer the questions. Write a summary. Read your summary to a partner.

World War I
Where did World War I start?

(1) World War I started in Europe in 1914. Many European countries were involved in the fighting. The Allied Powers were the countries of Great Britain, France, Belgium and Russia. The Central Powers were Germany, Austria-Hungary and the Ottoman Empire. The United States remained neutral, which means that it did not take sides, for several years. World War I is known as the first modern war because of the many changes in warfare brought about by new technology. The airplane, machine gun, submarine and tank changed the way wars were fought. America joined the Allies in 1917, after Germany started using their submarines to destroy American ships with torpedoes. Many Americans volunteered for the army and others were drafted, which means they were selected at random. With America's support, the Allies won the war. The fighting stopped on the eleventh hour of the eleventh day of the eleventh month in 1918.

(2) World War I affected America in many ways. Before America entered the war, American businesses made products to sell to the fighting countries. After America entered the war and men went off to fight, many jobs were left open. Many women went to work in offices and factories and many African-Americans moved to northern cities to fill jobs. This was called the great migration. Since many of those workers used to work on farms, farmers needed to hire replacements. They often hired Mexicans as migrant workers (workers who travel from place to place to harvest crops). The soldiers needed supplies and equipment to fight the war so Americans at home were encouraged to conserve resources. They began eating less food and driving their cars less to save gas. Women and children volunteered to collect books and clothes to send to the soldiers. These were some of the ways many Americans showed their patriotism.

ELD Standard
Describe main ideas and supporting details of a text.
ELA Standard
Discern main ideas and concepts presented in texts, identifying and assessing evidence that support those ideas.

1. World War I started in —
   - [ ] 1842
   - [ ] 1914
   - [ ] 1916
   - [ ] 1920

2. All of the following changed the way wars were fought except —
   - [ ] race cars
   - [ ] airplanes
   - [ ] machine guns
   - [ ] submarines

3. World War I affected America in the following way —
   - [ ] men worked on farms
   - [ ] American businesses closed down
   - [ ] women had to take men's jobs
   - [ ] women stayed home

4. Another good title for this article is —
   - [ ] The Neutral Countries
   - [ ] The Central Powers
   - [ ] America Enters into World War I
   - [ ] Women Work in Factories

5. If you wanted to know more about World War I, you should —
   - [ ] go to Great Britain
   - [ ] study a map
   - [ ] read a history book
   - [ ] read a science book

6. What is Paragraph 1 mainly about?
   - [ ] America entering World War I
   - [ ] American volunteers
   - [ ] migrant workers
   - [ ] American business

Summary

_____

_____

_____

_____

_____

Name _____   Date _____

ⓐ Persuasive Writing

World War I changed America. Many boys were persuaded to become soldiers by advertisements and posters expressing that the United States needed soldiers.

✔ Persuasive writing gives reasons to persuade someone to do something.

Writing Prompt

■ Create a poster and write an ad convincing boys to volunteer to become soldiers.

Before Writing: Make a list of the reasons why boys should become soldiers.
　　　　　　　　Ask yourself these questions:
　　　　　　　　　　What am I trying to persuade the person to do.
　　　　　　　　　　What facts can I use?
　　　　　　　　　　Which reasons are most important?

After Writing: Use the writing checklist at the back of the book.
　　　　　　　　Read your poster to a partner.

Reasons:

1. _____

2. _____

3. _____

4. _____

5. _____

6. _____

7. _____

ELD Standard
　Independently write a persuasive letter or essay with relevant information.
ELA Standard
　Write a persuasive letter or composition supporting a position with relevant information.

157

Poster

158

Name _____   Date _____

ⓐ Demonstrating Comprehension
Synonyms

- Read the passage and chart to a partner.
- Your partner sums up the main idea of the paragraph and reads each fact. Switch roles.
- Answer the questions on page 160.

The Roaring Twenties

The decade of the 1920s was called the "Roaring Twenties." Why? World War I had ended the previous decade and people had more money than ever before. So they had fun. Young people in their teens acted wildly. Women cut their hair short into "bobs." Girls and women wore dresses for the first time that actually showed their knees. Movies started showing in theaters in 1926. *Steamboat Willie* made by Walt Disney in 1928 featured Mickey Mouse. It was the first cartoon with a sound track. Radio also became popular in the 1920s. Along with movies and radio, there were many new inventions and foods that came upon the American scene during the 1920s. The following chart outlines some fascinating 1920s facts.

Some Fascinating 1920s Facts
✔ Earl Wise had too many potatoes. He peeled them, sliced them with a cabbage cutter and then fried them into the first potato chips. He sold them in brown paper bags.
✔ Model-T Fords were selling fast and accounted for half of the automobiles sold in 1920. Two million were sold in 1923.
✔ The first all-electric jukeboxes were blasting music in 1928.
✔ Air mail became a popular form of sending letters during the 1920s.
✔ The first Macy's Thanksgiving Day Parade was held in New York City in 1924.
✔ Bessie Smith, George Gershwin and Duke Ellington were popular musicians in the 1920s.
✔ Robert Goddard launched the first liquid fuel rocket in 1926.

1. What is the first paragraph mainly about?
   - [ ] World War I
   - [ ] the Great Depression
   - [ ] the Roaring 20s
   - [ ] the popsicle

2. If you wanted to know more about the Roaring 20s, you should —
   - [ ] read a history book
   - [ ] ask a toy store owner
   - [ ] read a sports magazine
   - [ ] look on a U.S. map

3. In this passage, a "bob" is a —
   - [ ] jukebox
   - [ ] parade
   - [ ] dress
   - [ ] haircut

4. Why did air mail become so popular?
   - [ ] because it cut the amount of time to send a letter long distance from weeks to days
   - [ ] because the cost of sending a letter became much less
   - [ ] because people always like to try new things
   - [ ] because people only started writing letters in the roaring '20s

5. According to the passage, which sentence describes best the "roaring twenties"?
   - [ ] Not much happened.
   - [ ] It was a decade of great prosperity.
   - [ ] It was a decade of great suffering.
   - [ ] Young people were very quiet.

6. All of these are facts about the 1920s except —
   - [ ] Earl Wise invented potato chips
   - [ ] Robert Goddard launched the first liquid rocket
   - [ ] people were fighting World War I
   - [ ] Model-T Fords were selling fast

✔ Synonyms are words that mean the same or almost the same as other words. For example, the words *rural* and *country* are synonyms.

■ Draw a line between the synonyms in column A and column B.

COLUMN A	COLUMN B
slice	ladies
movie	car
women	motion picture
fast	quickly
automobile	cut

ELD Standard
Read and identify text features, such as tables, tables of contents, chapter headings, diagrams and charts. Recognize simple antonyms and synonyms in written text.

ELA Standard
Understand how text features (e.g. format, graphics, sequence, diagrams, illustrations, charts, maps) make information accessible and usable. Use a thesaurus to identify alternative word choices and meanings.

Name _____   Date _____

b Creating a Chart

- Create a chart. List some fascinating facts about the 2000s.
- Read your facts to a partner.

Some Fascinating Facts in the 2000s

ELD Standard
Read and identify text features, such as tables, tables of contents, chapter headings, diagrams, and charts.
ELA Standard
Understand how text features (e.g., format, graphics, sequence, diagrams, illustrations, charts, maps) make information accessible and usable.

Name   Date
_____   _____

ⓐ Using Quotation Marks
Synonyms

━━ ━━ ━━ ━━ ━━ ━━ ━━ ━━ ━━ ━━ ━━ ━━ ━━ ━━ ━━ ━━

✔ Use quotation marks to show a speaker's exact words.

My brother Ben asked, "Didn't the Great Depression begin in 1929?"

Grandma answered, "Yes. Millions of people couldn't find work."

✔ Never use quotation marks when you do not use the speaker's exact words.

Grandpa thought the Great Depression was a terrible time.

✔ Never use quotation marks around words that tell who is speaking.

"Many people were homeless during the Great Depression," **said Grandma.**

The teacher told her to go home and eat. "I can't go home and eat," **replied the girl.** *"I have no food to eat."*

━━ ━━ ━━ ━━ ━━ ━━ ━━ ━━ ━━ ━━ ━━ ━━ ━━ ━━ ━━ ━━

▪ Rewrite each sentence.

▪ Add quotation marks where they belong.

▪ Read the sentences to a partner.

1. The unemployment problem was very severe during the Great Depression, said Grandpa.

   _____

2. Grandma said that many people lost all of their savings when the stock market crashed.

   _____

3. Were families evicted, or thrown out of their homes, when they couldn't pay the rent? asked Mama.

   _____

   _____

ELD Standard
   Edit writing for basic conventions. Recognize simple antonyms and synonyms in written text.
ELA Standard
   Use quotation marks around the exact words of a speaker and titles of poems, songs, short stories, and so forth. Use a thesaurus to identify alternative word choices and meanings.

4. Did you know that the owners of some companies lost so much money that they went out of business? asked Grandma.

_____

_____

5. In a mining town, a teacher told a hungry girl to go home and eat. I can't, the girl replied. It's my sister's day to eat.

_____

_____

6. The teacher explained, Because of the drought, the middle part of the United States became known as the Dust Bowl.

_____

_____

7. There was little money for schools during the Great Depression. Some classes were held in tin shacks, said the teacher.

_____

_____

8. Children made scooters out of orange crates, scraps of lumber and roller skate wheels, exclaimed Aunt Carol.

_____

_____

9. Did you know that during the Great Depression children mowed lawns for 25 cents? asked Grandpa.

_____

_____

10. Did you know children could go to the movies in the 1930s for one dime? asked Uncle Carlos.

_____

_____

11. Where I'm from in Texas, most people lost everything, my great uncle remembered. The terrible drought lasted many years. The dust storms destroyed their crops.

_____

_____

_____

12. My greatgrandparents said, Many hungry people stood in long lines to get free soup and bread.

_____

_____

■ One word in each sentence below is underlined. Look at the three words that appear in parentheses after each sentence.

■ One of these words is the synonym of the underlined word. Circle the synonym.

1. Dad said, "Your greatgrandfather owned a <u>company</u> before the Great Depression." (stock market   business   money)

2. The author wrote that people could not <u>buy</u> things from the stores. They didn't have any money. (purchase   sell   destroy)

3. "The Dust Bowl was caused by a <u>harsh</u> drought," remembered Grandma. (light   easy   severe)

4. The book *The Grapes of Wrath* describes a family who <u>moved</u> from Oklahoma to California. (relocated   went   drove)

5. My history book states, "The Great Depression in the U.S. <u>started</u> in 1929 and ended in 1941." (finished   terminated   began)

Name   Date
_____

a Prepositional Phrases

▬ ▬ ▬ ▬ ▬ ▬ ▬ ▬ ▬ ▬ ▬ ▬ ▬ ▬ ▬ ▬ ▬ ▬ ▬

✔ A preposition relates a noun or pronoun to another word in the sentence.

_in_ World War II   _above_ the clouds

✔ Here are some common prepositions:

about	around	for	on
above	at	from	over
across	behind	in	to
after	by	near	under
against	down	of	with

✔ A prepositional phrase begins with a preposition and ends with a noun or a pronoun.

_on_ the radio

▬ ▬ ▬ ▬ ▬ ▬ ▬ ▬ ▬ ▬ ▬ ▬ ▬ ▬ ▬ ▬ ▬ ▬ ▬

▪ Read each sentence to a partner.

▪ Underline the prepositional phrase in each sentence.

Beware   Some sentences have more than one prepositional phrase.

1. The broadcast on the radio stated that America had entered World War II.

2. Americans entered the war after Japan dropped bombs on Pearl Harbor.

3. The plane that dropped the bombs flew over Hawaii.

4. My friend's parents lived near Manila when Japanese troops invaded the Philippines.

5. American soldiers fought battles against German and Italian troops in Europe and Africa.

6. America dropped atomic bombs on two Japanese cities, Nagasake and Hiroshima.

7. German U-boats traveled under the ocean's surface. The U-boats, or submarines, sank many ships in the Atlantic Ocean.

ELD Standard
   Use correct parts of speech.
ELA Standard
   Identify and correctly use prepositional phrases, appositives, and independent and dependent clauses; use transitions and conjunctions to connect ideas.

Complete each sentence by choosing the correct prepositional phrase from the chart.

in tin cans	to the United States
under the porch	above the clouds
around the corner	after World War II
about the war	on the phone

1. During the war, 32,000 British children were sent _____.

2. There is a victory garden _____.

3. Many women continued working _____.

4. People saved meat fat _____.

5. The plane flew _____.

6. The children saved their cans and put them _____.

7. People from different countries talked to each other _____.

Name   Date

ⓐ Demonstrating Comprehension

- Read the passage to a partner. Your partner sums up the main idea after each paragraph. Switch roles.
- Your partner retells how to make ketchup.
- Read the questions on page 169 and then read the passage again.
- Answer the questions.
- Discuss your answers with a partner.

Victory Gardens

During World War II, people planted *victory gardens*. They grew food in vacant lots, backyards, zoos and playgrounds. Victory gardens were grown in support of the war effort. Since most of the farmers' crops were being shipped to the troops overseas, families grew their own food. Victory gardens were grown to support the farmers shipping their produce overseas.

People planted fruit and vegetables in their victory gardens. The gardens were thought of as a family's contribution to the soldier's victory overseas.

One victory garden that was planted in a playground grew such an abundance of tomatoes that the family didn't know what to do with them. One of the boys in the family suggested that the family make and bottle ketchup. Since ketchup is one of America's favorite sauces, the boys thought that the bottles of ketchup would be enjoyed by the soldiers. Here is the recipe the boys used to make ketchup.

ELD Standard
    Read and orally identify examples of fact/opinion, cause/effect in literature and content area texts.
ELA Standard
    Distinguish facts, supported inferences, and opinions in text.

Ketchup Recipe

This ketchup is the tastiest ketchup in America!

Ingredients for one batch of ketchup:

4 medium to large ripe tomatoes

1 small onion, peeled

$1/2$ sweet red pepper (sweet green pepper will also do)

$1/3$ cup sugar

$1/4$ teaspoon each of paprika, salt, allspice, ground cinnamon

dash of clove, celery salt, dry mustard

juice of $1/2$ lemon

Utensils:

2 quart pot

small kitchen knife

kitchen blender

measuring cups and spoons

mixing spoon

Steps:

1. Fill the pot half full of water. Add the tomatoes whole and bring them to a boil. Turn off the heat and allow the tomatoes to cool. Remove the tomatoes from the water and peel off the skins.

2. Cut the tomatoes, onion and sweet pepper into small chunks and mix them together until the mixture is very soupy. You may use a blender for this step.

3. Pour the mixture into the pot and add the remaining ingredients, except the lemon juice. Cook the mixture over low heat for about two hours, stirring every ten minutes, until the ketchup reaches desired thickness. Thick ketchup tastes best.

4. Add the lemon juice. Turn off the heat and let the ketchup cool. Put in a jar or bottle and refrigerate.

Homemade ketchup is darker than the store–bought kind and is tastier.

1. Which of these is an opinion in this recipe?
   - ☐ fill the pot half full of water
   - ☐ you need 1 small onion
   - ☐ you need utensils for this recipe
   - ☐ thick ketchup tastes the best

2. What do the directions say to do after you cut the tomatoes, onion and sweet pepper into small chunks?
   - ☐ fill the pot half full of water and add the tomatoes whole
   - ☐ refrigerate the ketchup
   - ☐ mix the ingredients until the mixture is soupy
   - ☐ add the lemon juice

3. Another good title for this recipe is —
   - ☐ Homemade Ketchup
   - ☐ Lemon Wedges
   - ☐ Hamburgers with Ketchup
   - ☐ The War Effort

4. If you wanted to find this recipe, you would look in a —
   - ☐ book about fruit
   - ☐ cookbook
   - ☐ travel magazine
   - history book

5. This article was written mainly to —
   - ☐ tell how to grow tomatoes
   - ☐ tell where to plant a victory garden
   - ☐ tell how ketchup was made during World War II
   - ☐ tell how to plant a victory garden

6. How long do you have to cook the tomato mixture?
   - ☐ 30 minutes
   - ☐ one hour
   - ☐ two hours
   - ☐ three hours

7. In step 2 of the recipe, what is a synonym for "cut into small chunks"?
   - ☐ boil
   - ☐ blend
   - ☐ slice
   - ☐ dice

8. If you wanted to make two batches of ketchup, what would you need to do?
   - ☐ use a large kitchen knife
   - ☐ pour juice of a $1/4$ lemon
   - ☐ add one whole sweet red pepper
   - ☐ boil the tomatoes in a smaller pot

169

Name _____   Date _____

a Demonstrating Comprehension
Antonyms

- Read the questions first. Then read the passage with a partner.
  Your partner sums up the main idea of each paragraph. Switch roles.

- Your partner retells the rules for submitting an article to *United Nations Children's Magazine*.

- Answer the questions.

- Discuss your answers with a partner.

United Nations Children's Magazine
A Magazine by and for Young Writers Around the World

(1) The United Nations is an international organization of countries that have promised to cooperate and make the world a peaceful and safe place. The headquarters of the United Nations is in New York City. Each member nation sends an ambassador to represent it and vote on important issues.

(2) The United Nations Children's Magazine reflects the beliefs of the United Nations in wanting world peace. The magazine publishes articles by young writers from around the world. Articles must be related to how the writer is helping to encourage world peace where he or she lives.

(3) If you would like to submit an article to the *United Nations Children's Magazine*, read the information on the next page.

ELD Standard
Use resources in the text (such as ideas, illustrations, titles) to draw conclusions and make inferences. Recognize simple antonyms and synonyms in written text.
ELA Standard
Draw inferences, conclusions or generalizations about text and support them with textual evidence and prior knowledge. Use a thesaurus to identify alternative word choices and meanings.

United Nations Children's Magazine

1. Children ages nine to fifteen may submit their artwork or writing.

2. We publish fiction, nonfiction, poetry and artwork. There is no limit to the length of materials submitted.

3. All material must be your own work. Text should be neatly written or typed. Include your name, address, and age with each work you submit.

4. When you send in stories, please indicate whether your work is fiction or nonfiction.

5. Send samples of your artwork if you are interested in illustrating poems. Paintings or drawings are acceptable.

6. Please include a self-addressed envelope if you want your work returned.

7. If any of your work is published in the *United Nations Children's Magazine*, you will receive ten free copies of the magazine.

8. Send all articles to:
United Nations Children's Magazine
P.O. Box 521
New York, NY 10001
U.S.A.

1. Those interested in illustrating poems should —
   - ☐ write to the publisher
   - ☐ send in their name and address
   - ☐ send in their name
   - ☐ send samples of their artwork

2. Stories that are sent in must be —
   - ☐ the writer's original work
   - ☐ fiction
   - ☐ fewer than 4 pages
   - ☐ illustrated

3. These directions were written in order to —
   - ☐ tell how to write a story
   - ☐ give guidelines
   - ☐ sell a magazine
   - ☐ give art lessons

4. Which of these would not be eligible for publication?
   - ☐ a poem written by a nine year old
   - ☐ a poem written by a ten year old
   - ☐ an article written by a sixteen year old
   - ☐ an article written by an eleven year old

5. Where can you buy *United Nations Children's Magazine?*
   - ☐ at the market
   - ☐ at the book store
   - ☐ through the mail
   - ☐ the directions do not say

6. What is a synonym for the word *beliefs* in paragraph 2?
   - ☐ promises
   - ☐ opinion
   - ☐ religion
   - ☐ responsibilities

✔ An **antonym** is a word that means the opposite of another word. For example, the words *tall* and *short* are antonyms.

■ Choose the correct antonym.

1. united
   - ☐ together
   - ☐ divided

2. peace
   - ☐ safe
   - ☐ war

3. encourage
   - ☐ cooperate
   - ☐ discourage

4. old
   - ☐ ancient
   - ☐ young

172

Name _____   Date _____

ⓑ Writing a Persuasive Essay

▬ ▬ ▬ ▬ ▬ ▬ ▬ ▬ ▬ ▬ ▬ ▬ ▬ ▬ ▬ ▬ ▬ ▬

Writing Prompt

■ Write a persuasive essay on *"What people must do to make the world a safe and peaceful place."* Start your essay below. Rewrite your final draft on a separate sheet of paper. Follow the rules of the contest on page 171.

Before Writing: Make a mind map on how to make the world a safe and peaceful place.

After Writing: Use the writing checklist at the back of the book.
      Have a partner use the writing checklist to edit your work.
      Read your essay to a partner.

How to make the world a safe and peaceful place

How to Make the World a Safe and Peaceful Place

By _____

_____

_____

_____

_____

_____

ELD Standard
  Begin to use a variety of genres in writing.
ELA Standard
  Write persuasive letters or compositions. Support a position with relevant evidence.

Name   Date

ⓐ Combining Sentences

▬▬ ▬▬ ▬ ▬ ▬▬ ▬▬ ▬ ▬ ▬▬ ▬▬ ▬ ▬ ▬▬ ▬▬ ▬ ▬ ▬▬ ▬▬

Use the word _and_ or _but_ to connect two sentences.

✔ *And* means "in addition."

People settled in communities in the 1950s. They built new homes.

Combine the two sentences with <u>and</u>.

People settled in communities in the 1950s, <u>and</u> they built new homes.

✔ *But* shows a contrast.

Some people wanted big houses. Others wanted small houses.

Combine the two sentences with <u>but</u>.

Some people wanted big houses, <u>but</u> others wanted small houses.

Use only one _and_ or _but_ in a sentence.

▬▬ ▬▬ ▬ ▬ ▬▬ ▬▬ ▬ ▬ ▬▬ ▬▬ ▬ ▬ ▬▬ ▬▬ ▬ ▬ ▬▬ ▬▬

▪ Combine each pair of sentences with <u>and</u> or <u>but</u>.
Rewrite the resulting sentences on the lines provided.

1. Children played with hula-hoops. They played with new toys.

   _____

2. Drag racing with hot rod cars was very popular in the 1950s. Many boys and girls had hot rod cars.

   _____

   _____

3. American people watched television. They listened to the radio.

   _____

ELD Standard
      Use correct parts of speech.
ELA Standard
      Identify and correctly use prepositional phrases, appositives, and independent and dependent clauses; use transitions
      and conjunctions to connect ideas.

4. Some Americans moved to live in cities in the 1950s. Others moved to live in suburbs.

_____

_____

5. In the beginning of 1950, there were 3 million televisions sets in the United States. By the end of 1950, there were 7 million sets.

_____

_____

6. Some Americans took vacations in the 1950s. Others stayed home.

_____

7. Davy Crockett was a hit with the kids in 1954. They all bought Davy Crockett hats.

_____

8. Howdy Doody was a television show in the 1950s. So was Captain Kangaroo.

_____

9. Rock and roll was great music in the 1950s. Some people couldn't dance.

_____

10. The Supreme Court in 1954 desegregated the schools. Children of all races went to school together.

_____

_____

Name _____   Date _____

a Writing Sentences of Fact and Opinion

▬ ▬

✔ A <u>fact</u> is a sentence that is true.

Scientists from the Soviet Union launched a satellite named Sputnik into space in October of 1957.

✔ An <u>opinion</u> is what someone thinks or feels.

Scientists from the Soviet Union are the smartest scientists in the world.

▬ ▬

- Read the passage to a partner. Read the passage to yourself.
- Write two facts and two opinions from the passage.
- Read the facts and opinions to a partner.

The Space Race
America's astronauts are the best in the world.

The belief that American astronauts are the best in the world was shaken when the Soviet Union launched a satellite called Sputnik into space in October of 1957. One month later, the Soviets launched another satellite with a dog on board.

NASA was created in 1958 in the USA to study space travel. America was concerned that the Soviets were too far ahead of them in exploring space. American scientists are better than any scientists in the world. The Americans, therefore, had to be first in the space race. The Soviets and the Americans competed to put the first astronaut in space. The Americans were successful in having the first astronaut to orbit and walk on the moon.

Fact: _____

Fact: _____

Opinion: _____

Opinion: _____

ELD Standard
Read and orally identify examples of fact/opinion and cause/effect in literature and content area texts.
ELA Standard
Distinguish facts, supported inferences and opinions in text.

Name _____   Date _____

ⓐ Demonstrating Comprehension

They Fought for Freedom
Children in the Civil Rights Movement

(1)   During the 1950s and 1960s, many people in the United States were <u>fighting for</u> civil rights. There was a tremendous amount of discrimination against African-American people, especially in some parts of the South. There were all kinds of laws which kept the races apart. This separation was called segregation. There were separate schools for whites and for blacks. There were separate places to eat, separate seating on buses and even separate water fountains. There were also laws which <u>prevented</u> African-Americans from registering to vote.

(2)   Many people realized that this was terribly unfair. They decided to put an end to segregation. They wanted African-Americans to have equal opportunity to go to school with other Americans, to eat with other Americans, to choose any seat on the bus, and to vote. They wanted integration—all races to mix freely.

(3)   People who wanted integration instead of segregation joined together and formed organizations like the Congress of Racial Equality (CORE), the Southern Christian Leadership Conference (SNCC) (which was headed by Dr. Martin Luther King, Jr.) and the National Association for the Advancement of Colored People (NAACP). These groups were determined to end segregation by peaceful protests. They planned demonstrations, marches and sit-ins. Sometimes they boycotted companies or stores that would not treat African-Americans fairly.

(4)   Men, women and children took part in these struggles for equal rights. Sometimes, people <u>protested</u> in their own small ways, with or without advanced planning. At other times, the protests were carefully-planned group activities. There are many stories of children who helped fight for civil rights. Gwendolyn Patton, Ernest Green, Claudette Colvin, Audrey Faye Hendricks, Larry Russell and Judy Tarver are just a few of the hundreds of children who were part of the civil rights movement.

ELD Standard
   Read and use detailed sentences to orally identify main ideas and use them to make predictions and provide supporting details for predictions made.
ELA Standard
   Discern main ideas and concepts presented in texts, identifying and assessing evidence that supports these ideas.

■ Fill in the bubble for each correct answer.

■ Reread the story to a partner.

1. You would most likely find this article in a —
   - [ ] history book
   - [ ] travel magazine
   - [ ] science book
   - [ ] math book

2. In this article, <u>protest</u> means —
   - [ ] demonstrate against something
   - [ ] protect people against an attack
   - [ ] be honest
   - [ ] approve of something

3. During the 1950s and 1960s, many people were fighting for —
   - [ ] Texas
   - [ ] the right to go overseas
   - [ ] farm workers
   - [ ] racial equality

4. Another good title for this article is —
   - [ ] The Conference
   - [ ] The Friends
   - [ ] Equal Treatment for Everyone
   - [ ] The Vietnam War

5. Martin Luther King, Jr. wanted to end segregation by —
   - [ ] making people angry
   - [ ] peaceful protests
   - [ ] strikes
   - [ ] violent demonstrations

6. Why did the author write this passage?
   - [ ] to persuade people to fight for everyone's civil rights
   - [ ] to explain how people strove for equality
   - [ ] to sell you a product
   - [ ] to describe segregation

7. A person who participates in the civil rights movement might say, —
   - [ ] "We should not allow people to protest."
   - [ ] "People shouldn't boycott stores. It would affect the economy negatively."
   - [ ] "Sometimes strikes are effective. Let's go on strike!"
   - [ ] "Society must give children of all races and religions the same opportunities."

8. Paragraph 3 uses the word "prevented." What is an antonym of "prevented"?
   - [ ] forbade
   - [ ] protested
   - [ ] permitted
   - [ ] boycotted

Name _____   Date _____

b Informative Writing

✔ Informative writing gives you information about something.

Writing Prompt

- Write a summary about this article.

    Before Writing: Complete the main idea mapping chart on the following page.

    After Writing: Use the writing checklist at the back of the book.
    Have a partner use the writing checklist to edit your work.
    Read your summary to a partner.

- Write a summary.

_____

_____

_____

_____

_____

_____

_____

_____

ELD Standard
    Write a brief narrative.
ELA Standard
    Create multiple-paragraph narrative compositions.

Main Idea Mapping Chart

Paragraph One: Main Idea

Detail

Detail

Detail

Paragraph Two: Main Idea

Detail

Detail

Detail

Paragraph Three: Main Idea

Detail

Detail

Detail

Paragraph Four: Main Idea

Detail

Detail

Detail

ELD Standard
Write a brief narrative. Read and use detailed sentences to orally identify main ideas and use them to make predictions and provide supporting details for predictions made.

ELA Standard
Create multiple-paragraph narrative compositions. Discern main ideas and concepts presented in texts, identifying and assessing evidence that supports these ideas.

Name _____   Date _____

a Parts of a Book

Title Page	the first page of a book; it tells the title, author and publisher of the book
Copyright Page	page after the title page; it tells the date that the book was published
Table of Contents	lists the chapters and page numbers
Body	the main part of a book
Glossary	defines special words in a book
Index	lists topics alphabetically and page numbers where these topics can be found

Title Page

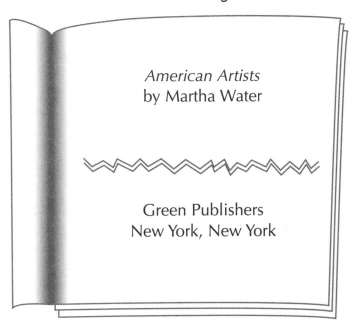

American Artists
by Martha Water

Green Publishers
New York, New York

Glosssary

Architect – one who designs buildings and advises in their construction

Artist – one who professes or practices an imaginative art

Composer – one who composes, a person who writes music

Musician – composer, conductor, or performer of music

Index

Architects 200

Artists 210

Composers 240

Dancers 115

Musicians 90

Photographers 80

Scupltors 5

- Discuss the parts of a book.
- Use the title page, glossary and index on pages 181 and 182 to answer each question below.
- Read your answers to a partner.

1. What is the title of this book?

_____

2. Who is the publisher of this book?

_____

3. On what page can you find information about musicians?

_____

4. What is the definition of an architect?

_____

5. Where is the publisher of this book located?

_____

6. On what page can you find information about photographers?

_____

7. Who is the author of the book *American Artists?*

_____

8. What is the definition of a musician?

_____

Name _____   Date _____

a Demonstrating Comprehension

Apple Pie Recipe

There is nothing as American as homemade apple pie.

Ingredients:
   2 cups flour
   3 tablespoons ice water
   $1/2$ cup butter or margarine
   8 apples, cored and sliced
   $1/2$ cup sugar
   1 teaspoon cinnamon

1. Mix the flour, half of the butter or margarine and the water together. Form the dough into a ball.
2. Roll half of the dough on a floured board.
3. Place the dough on the bottom of a pie pan.
4. Put the apples on top of the dough.
5. Mix the sugar and cinnamon together. Put the mixture on top of the apples.
6. Put $1/4$ cup of butter or margarine on top of the apples.
7. Roll out the rest of the dough and place it on top of the apples.
8. Cut slits in the top of the piecrust.
9. Bake the pie in the oven at 350° for 35–45 minutes.
10. Eat the pie. Enjoy!

1. How much butter or margarine do you put on top of the sliced apples?
   - ☐ 2 cups
   - ☐ 1 cup
   - ☐ $1/2$ cup
   - ☐ $1/4$ cup

2. The information in this recipe was written in order to —
   - ☐ tell you how to make apple pie
   - ☐ describe how to serve apple pie
   - ☐ tell you how to cut apples
   - ☐ teach you how to read a recipe

3. Apple pie would probably taste best with —
   - ☐ string beans
   - ☐ corn
   - ☐ pickles
   - ☐ ice cream

4. In the recipe, which of these is an opinion?
   - ☐ The pie must bake for 35–45 minutes.
   - ☐ You must mix the flour with the margarine.
   - ☐ There is nothing that is as American as homemade apple pie.
   - ☐ There are eight apples needed for this recipe.

5. The apples in this recipe must be —
   - ☐ sliced and stacked
   - ☐ cored and sliced
   - ☐ picked and packed
   - ☐ cored and canned

6. Apple pie is best served as a —
   - ☐ dinner
   - ☐ drink
   - ☐ soup
   - ☐ dessert

7. Why would someone want to read this recipe?
   - ☐ to find out why apple pie is a popular food in the U.S.
   - ☐ to make apple pie for an Independence Day picnic
   - ☐ to learn how to make crust for blueberry pie
   - ☐ to form an opinion of apple pie

8. What would the pie be like if you added more sugar?
   - ☐ The pie would taste sweeter.
   - ☐ The pie would be more difficult to make.
   - ☐ The pie would need add more apples.
   - ☐ The pie would need lemon.

ELD Standard
Read and orally identify examples of fact/opinion and cause/effect in literature and in content area texts.
ELA Standard
Distinguish facts, supported inferences and opinions in text.

Name _____   Date _____

b Descriptive Writing

✔ *Descriptive writing* tells how something looks, feels, smells, sounds and tastes.
  It paints a word picture for the reader.

Writing Prompt

■ Describe your favorite dessert. Use as many adjectives or descriptive words as possible.

Before Writing: Make a mind map to list all the adjectives that describe your favorite dessert.

After Writing: Use the writing checklist at the back of the book.
                 Read your description to a partner.

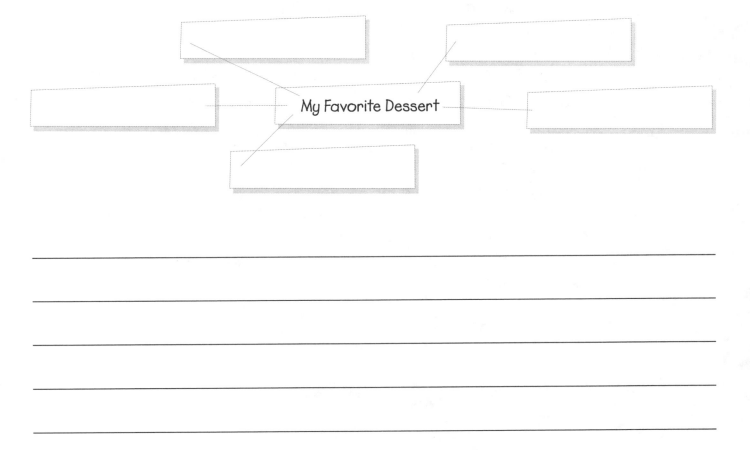

My Favorite Dessert

_____

_____

_____

_____

_____

_____

ELD Standard
    Write a brief narrative.
ELA Standard
    Develop the topic with simple facts, details, examples, and explanations.

Name   Date

ⓐ Demonstrating Comprehension

━ ━ ━ ━ ━ ━ ━ ━ ━ ━ ━ ━ ━ ━ ━ ━ ━

An innovation is a device or idea that allows people to do things in a different way than they did before. The telephone and the electric light are two inventions or innovations.

Innovations
A Magazine for Young Inventors

If you would like to submit your invention to *Innovation Magazine*, read the information below.

1. Children ages ten to fifteen may send a picture and a description of their invention.

2. All inventions must be original.

3. All inventions must include your name, address and age.

4. There is no limit to the number of inventions you may submit.

5. If you are interested in writing reviews of the inventions that are accepted by *Innovations Magazine*, send your name, address, age and phone number to the address listed below.

6. Please include a self-addressed envelope so that you can be notified if your invention is selected for the magazine.

7. If your invention is published in the magazine, you will receive ten free copies of that issue.

8. Send all pictures with descriptions of your invention to:

> *Innovations Magazine*
> P.O. Box 1732
> Sacramento, CA 95855

ELD Standard
    Describe main ideas and supporting details, including supporting evidence.
ELA Standard
    Draw inferences, conclusions or generalizations about text and support them with textual evidence and prior knowledge.

■ Fill in the bubble for each correct answer.

1. This article was written in order to —
   ☐ give directions to the magazine office
   ☐ give guidelines
   ☐ tell how to create an invention
   ☐ sell a magazine

2. Which of these inventions would <u>not</u> be eligible for publication in the magazine?
   ☐ an invention created by a thirteen year old girl
   ☐ an invention that is useful
   ☐ an invention that is original
   ☐ an invention created by a nine year old boy

3. Those interested in writing reviews of the inventions should —
   ☐ watch the video on inventions
   ☐ have their teacher call the magazine
   ☐ send your name, address, age and phone number to the magazine
   ☐ send a picture of your invention

4. Inventions sent in must —
   ☐ be made of wood
   ☐ include a description
   ☐ be copied from someone else
   ☐ be small

5. Where could you buy *Innovations Magazine*?
   ☐ at the library
   ☐ at the gas station
   ☐ at the zoo
   ☐ the directions do not say

6. Whoever's invention is chosen for publication will receive —
   ☐ ten free copies of the magazine
   ☐ three free copies of the magazine
   ☐ $35.00
   ☐ a free subscription to the magazine

7. Why do people invent things?
   ☐ because they are looking for solutions to problems
   ☐ because they have unique, innovative ideas
   ☐ because new technology helps industry stay competitive
   ☐ All of the above.

8. What would <u>not</u> be a new invention in the early 21st century?
   ☐ an automobile that flies through the air
   ☐ a house that uses sunlight for electricity
   ☐ a medicine that will help us live until we reach 200 years old
   ☐ an airplane that can fly around the world in two hours

Name _____   Date _____

b Descriptive Writing

Descriptive Writing

✔ Descriptive writing describes how something looks, feels, tastes, sounds or smells.

Writing Prompt

- Create a drawing of an original invention.
- Write a description of how to use your invention.
- Write your name, address and age at the bottom of your description.
- Read your description to a partner.

ELD Standard
   Begin to use a variety of genres in writing.
ELA Standard
   Write narrative expository, persuasive and descriptive texts.

Name _____   Date _____

ⓐ Demonstrating Comprehension

Famous Inventions

Three important inventions that have changed life in
America are the camera, the telephone and the electric light.

The Camera

The camera was not invented by any single person. Many different people, over
a period of 200 years, contributed to the camera as we know it today. Taking
pictures with a camera is called photography. The word *photography* means
to make pictures with light. The first camera that was available to the general
public was made in 1888 by George Eastman in New York.

The basic parts of the camera are the lens, the shutter and the film. The lens is
a special piece of glass that allows the light to shine on the film inside the
camera box. The shutter controls the amount of light that is used to make the
picture. When it is time to take a picture, the photographer pushes a button to
open the shutter and expose the film, which is sensitive to light. After the film is
exposed, it is removed from the camera and sent to be developed. The
developed film is then used to print pictures.

The camera changed American life because with it people could take pictures
of each other and keep the pictures to remember the good times they had.
They could also use photos to illustrate newspaper stories. The camera made
it possible to see what was happening across America and around the world.

The Telephone

The second invention that changed American life was the telephone. Humans
have always wanted to communicate over long distances. People have used
smoke signals, mirrors, jungle drums, carrier pigeons and flags to send
messages. In 1876, in Boston, Massachusetts, Alexander Graham Bell invented a
tool, which used sound to make a signal that would travel through a wire to
people far away. He called his invention the telephone, which means, "far away

ELD Standard
   Describe main ideas and supporting details, including supporting evidence.
ELA Standard
   Discern main ideas and concepts presented in texts, identifying and assessing evidence that supports those ideas.

voice." When *you* use a telephone, vibrations move through the air and into the mouthpiece, sending a signal through the telephone wire, causing the ear piece of the listener's telephone to vibrate. Then, the listener hears your voice.

The telephone made it possible to talk to people across the United States and around the world.

<h3 style="text-align:center">The Electric Light</h3>

The third invention was the electric light. Before the invention of the electric light, people used oil lamps and natural gas for light. For at least fifty years, inventors had experimented with some sort of electric light but no one was successful. From 1878 to 1880, inventor Thomas Edison and his associates tried at least 3,000 different materials while developing the electric light. The lamp was made of tiny wire inside a glass bulb. On October 21, 1879, he and his workers were ready to test their light bulb. Electricity was applied to the glass bulb and it immediately began to glow with a soft orange light. This first test lasted thirteen hours before the tiny wire broke. Thomas Edison built a factory to make light bulbs for everyone.

1. You would most likely find these articles in a —
   - [ ] fashion magazine
   - [ ] history book
   - [ ] travel magazine
   - [ ] literature textbook

2. What is the second paragraph of *The Camera* mainly about?
   - [ ] the electric light
   - [ ] how the camera changed American life
   - [ ] the basic parts of a photographic camera
   - [ ] the first camera

3. Another good title for *The Telephone* is —
   - [ ] Different Ways to Use the Telephone
   - [ ] The Telephone Changed America
   - [ ] How Telephones and Other Inventions Changed American Life
   - [ ] Alexander Graham Bell and His Life in Boston

4. What is one result of the electric light?
   - [ ] People don't have to read by candlelight.
   - [ ] People can go out at night without flashlights.
   - [ ] Light bulbs glow for more than three hours.
   - [ ] Factories make light bulbs faster and more efficiently.

5. The web shows some important ideas in the article.

Famous Inventions

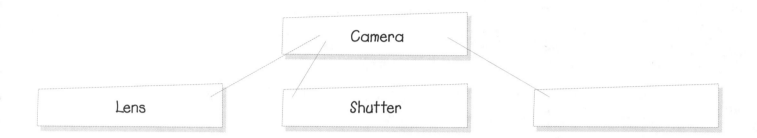

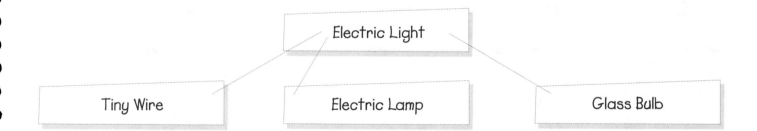

Which of these belongs in the empty box?
- ☐ Inventor
- ☐ Bulbs
- ☐ Film
- ☐ Mirrors

Name _____ Date _____

ⓐ Writing Dialogue

▬▬ ▬ ▬▬ ▬ ▬▬ ▬▬ ▬ ▬▬ ▬▬ ▬ ▬▬ ▬▬ ▬▬ ▬▬ ▬ ▬▬ ▬

✔ Use quotation marks to show a speaker's exact words.

The girl answered the phone and said, "Hello. How are you?"

✔ Never use quotation marks around words that tell who is speaking.

"I can't believe I'm talking to you on the telephone," said the man.

✔ Do not use quotation marks when you do not use the speaker's exact words.

My grandmother said she was coming to visit.

✔ When you write a dialogue or conversation, you use quotation marks to show a person's exact words.

My dad called home and said, "Let's go to the baseball game."

✔ Quotation marks go at the beginning and the end of the person's exact words.

My friend asked, "Who invented the telephone?"

✔ Begin the person's words with a capital letter. Finish the sentence with a quotation mark.

Mom called me on the cellular phone and said, "Please come home now!"

✔ End the person's words with a period, question mark, or exclamation point if the quote comes at the end of a sentence.

In the first telephone call, Alexander Graham Bell said, "Mr. Watson, come here. I want you!"

✔ End the person's words with a comma if the quote is followed by *said* _____.

"You need to insert 25 cents for the next three minutes," said the operator.

▬▬ ▬ ▬▬ ▬ ▬▬ ▬▬ ▬ ▬▬ ▬▬ ▬ ▬▬ ▬▬ ▬▬ ▬▬ ▬ ▬▬ ▬

Writing Prompt

■ Imagine the first conversation that a typical person spoke over the telephone. Write the conversation between two people.

Before Writing: Think of what the two people may have said.
　　　　　　　　Use quotation marks around what the people said.

After Writing: Use the writing checklist at the back of the book.
　　　　　　　Read the conversation to a partner.

ELD Standard
　　Begin to use a variety of genres in writing.
ELA Standard
　　Students write narrative, expository and descriptive texts.

The First Telephone Conversation

The first telephone conversation was between _____ and _____ .

This is the conversation. _____

_____

_____

_____

_____

_____

_____

_____

_____

_____

_____

_____

_____

Name _____   Date _____

a Irregular Verbs

▬ ▬ ▬ ▬ ▬ ▬ ▬ ▬ ▬ ▬ ▬ ▬ ▬ ▬ ▬ ▬ ▬

✔ You make a verb past tense by adding _ed_ (or _d_ if the word ends in _e_.)

I play<u>ed</u> on the playground.   *I wire<u>d</u> the invention.*

✔ There are some verbs that don't follow this rule. These are irregular verbs.

Present	Past	Past with has, have or had
build	built	has, have or had built
draw	drew	has, have or had drawn
drive	drove	has, have or had driven
know	knew	has, have or had known
think	thought	has, have or had thought
speed	sped	has, have or had sped
spin	spun	has, have or had spun
sweep	swept	has, have or had swept

■ Write the correct irregular past tense verb from the chart in each sentence.

■ Read the sentence to a partner.

1. The first vehicle with an engine was _____ in 1769 in France.

2. The man _____ the vehicle two miles down the road.

3. The first car could not have _____ down the freeway.

4. In the 1880s engineers _____ that their cars needed a faster engine.

5. When the car hit ice, it _____ around and around.

6. Mr. Henry Ford _____ up the idea of making cars on the assembly line.

194

ELD Standard
    Identify parts of speech.
ELA Standard
    Identify and correctly use verbs, modifiers and pronouns.

Name _____ Date _____

◧ Using a Thesaurus

✔ A thesaurus can help you find synonyms and antonyms of a word. The entries are organized in alphabetical order.

✔ Remember that a synonym is a word that means the same as or similar to another word. *Big* and *large* are synonyms.

✔ Remember that an antonym is a word that means the opposite of another word. *Big* and *little* are antonyms.

✔ At the top of a thesaurus page are two guide words. The first guide word is the first entry word on the page. The second word is the last entry word on that page.

✔ A thesaurus might include the part of speech (noun, verb, adjective) and a sentence that helps you learn to use the word.

modern – monstruous 151

modern *adjective — Synonym* new, recent, contemporary, present-day
Antonym ancient, old, antique

Modern ideas of engineering made the automobile possible.

▪ Ask and answer the questions with a partner.

1. What is the first word on this thesaurus page? _____

2. What is the last word on this thesaurus page? _____

3. What part of speech does this thesaurus give for the word *modern?* _____

ELD Standard
Use a standard thesaurus to find the meanings of known vocabulary.
ELA Standard
Use a thesaurus to identify alternative word choices and meanings.

4. How many synonyms does this thesaurus give for *modern?* _____

5. How many antonyms does this thesaurus give for *modern?* _____

6. What page of this thesaurus do you think the word *machine* appears?

   Page 148 or 152? _____

7. Go to the class thesaurus. Write the synonyms for the following words:

   build _____

   _____

   automobile _____

   _____

   bright _____

   _____

   travel _____

   _____

■ Use one synonym from each word in a sentence.

   _____

   _____

   _____

Name _____   Date _____

ⓐ Indefinite Pronouns

Indefinite Pronouns

✔ Pronouns that do not refer to any definite person or thing are called <u>indefinite pronouns</u>.

each   *none*   *many*   *another*   *some*

✔ Some indefinite pronouns are <u>singular</u>: *each, none, somebody, something, another.*

✔ Some indefinite pronouns are <u>plural</u>: *several, many, both, some.*

■ Underline the indefinite pronouns in these sentences.

■ On the line that follows each sentence, write if the indefinite pronoun is singular (refers to one person or thing) or plural (refers to more than one person or thing).

Example: *<u>Several</u> were asked about the development of the camera.*

1. Many contributed to the development of the camera.   _____plural_____

2. Each of us took pictures with the camera.   _____

3. Something is in the photo that I can't see.   _____

4. None of the cameras is digital.   _____

5. Somebody adjusted the lens of the camera.   _____

6. Both of us bought film for the camera.   _____

7. Several knew the word *"photography"* means
   "to make pictures with light."   _____

8. Some know that the basic parts of a camera are
   the lens, shutter and the film.   _____

ELD Standard
   Identify parts of speech.
ELA Standard
   Identify and correctly use verbs that are often misused, modifiers, and pronouns.

■ Use each of these indefinite pronouns in a sentence.

■ Remember that singular indefinite pronouns take the singular form of the verb.

none   *several*   *each*   *both*   *another*

1. _____

_____

2. _____

_____

3. _____

_____

4. _____

_____

5. _____

_____

Name   Date

a Writing a Narrative

Narrative Writing

✔ Narrative writing tells a story. The story has a beginning, a middle and an end.
  It has characters, events and an ending.

Writing Prompt

▪ Think of a movie you have seen on television. Write a story that tells what happened in the movie. Tell the story using the main idea of what happened in the movie and the most significant details.

Before Writing: Make a story map of the movie on page 200.
Answer the following questions on the story map.
Who were the characters?
What was the setting?
What were the events that happened?
Did the characters have a problem?
What was the ending to the movie?

▪ On page 200, draw three pictures about the movie you've seen on television. Draw the beginning of the movie, the main idea of the movie and the ending of the movie.

After Writing: Use the writing checklist to edit your work.
Ask a partner to use the writing checklist to edit your work.
Read your story to a partner.

ELD Standard
    Write short narrative stories that include elements of setting and character.
ELA Standard
    Write narratives. Show and tell the events of the story.

Pre-Writing Story Map

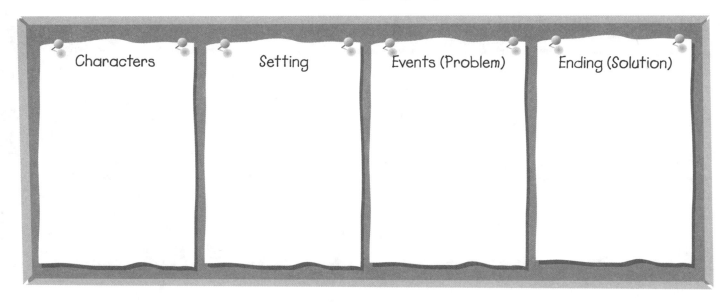

Title of Television Movie

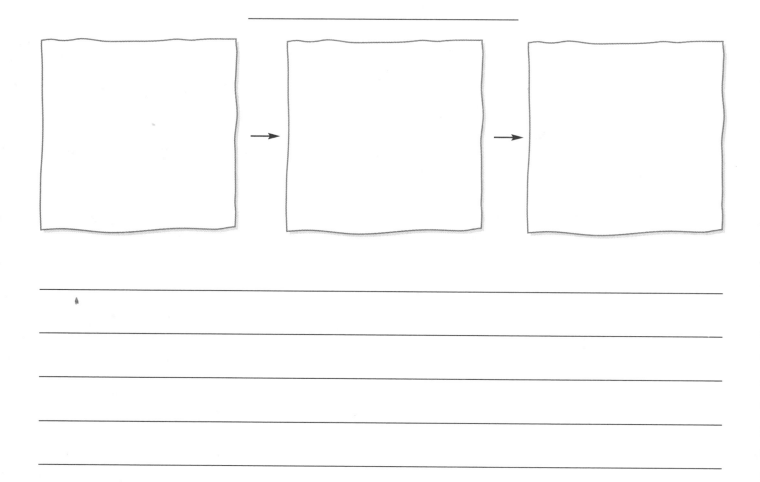

Name _____   Date _____

a Demonstrating Comprehension/Narrative Writing

How We Made the First Flight (Edited Fragment)

By Orville Wright

(1) The course of the flight up and down was
exceedingly erratic, partly due to the
irregularity of the air, and partly to lack of
experience in handling this machine. The control
of the front rudder was difficult because it is
balanced too close to the center. This gave it a
tendency to turn itself when started so that it
turned too far on one side and then too far on
the other. As a result, the machine would rise
<u>suddenly</u> to about ten feet, and then as suddenly
dart for the ground. A sudden dart when a little

over a hundred feet from the end of the track, or a little over 120 feet from the point at
which it rose into the air, ended the flight. The velocity of the wind was over 35 feet per
second. The speed of the machine over the ground against this wind was ten feet per
second. The speed of the machine relative to the air was over 45 feet per second, and the
length of the flight was equivalent to a flight of 540 feet made in calm air. This flight lasted
only 12 seconds, but it was nevertheless the first in the history of the world in which a
machine carrying a man had raised itself by its own power into the air in full flight, had sailed
forward without reduction of speed and had finally landed at a point as high as that from
which it started.

(2) With the <u>assistance</u> of our visitors, we carried the machine back to the track and prepared
for another flight. The <u>stinging</u> wind, however, had chilled us all through, so that before
attempting a second flight, we all went to the building again to warm ourselves. Johnny Ward,
seeing under the table a box filled with eggs, asked one of the station men where we got so
many of them. The people of the neighborhood eke out a bare existence by catching fish
during the short fishing season, and their supplies of other articles of food are limited. He
had probably never seen so many eggs at one time in his whole life. One person asked him if he

ELD Standard
     Generate and respond to comprehension questions related to text.
ELA Standard
     Describe the function and effect of common literary devices.

had noticed a small hen running about the outside of the building. "That chicken lays eight to ten eggs a day!" Ward, having just seen a piece of machinery lift itself from the ground and fly, a thing at that time considered as impossible as perpetual motion, was ready to believe nearly anything. But after going out and having a good look at the wonderful fowl, he returned with the remark, "It's only a common looking chicken!"

Source: The Aviation Education Clearinghouse of the Federal Aviation Administration.

1. Why did Orville Wright write *How We Made the First Flight?*
   - [ ] to describe what happened during and after the first airplane flight
   - [ ] to convince people that airplanes are difficult to fly
   - [ ] to show that that people who witnessed the first flight were amazed at what they saw
   - [ ] to describe the velocity of the wind and the speed of the airplane

2. What was Orville Wright's main problem?
   - [ ] to control the airplane
   - [ ] to keep the airplane in the sky for a long time
   - [ ] to land the airplane
   - [ ] to prepare the airplane for a second flight

3. How did the visitors react to the event?
   - [ ] with sadness
   - [ ] with amazement
   - [ ] with fear
   - [ ] with laughter

4. What would be a good way to end the first paragraph?
   - [ ] The flight was a historic moment for all humanity.
   - [ ] The flight was very long and tiring.
   - [ ] We were very happy and wanted to do it again. So we did!
   - [ ] Many people tried to fly before us, but we were the most successful.

5. How was the climate?
   - [ ] hot
   - [ ] cold
   - [ ] warm
   - [ ] snowy

6. Look at the word <u>suddenly</u> in paragraph 1. What are antonyms for this word?
   - [ ] quickly and independently
   - [ ] calmly and with difficulty
   - [ ] expectedly and slowly
   - [ ] erratically and dangerously

7. Look at the word <u>assistance</u> in paragraph 2. What is a synonym for this word?
   - ☐ attendance
   - ☐ help
   - ☐ hindrance
   - ☐ preparation

8. What would be a good metaphor for this story?
   - ☐ A ship plows the sea with a catch of fish.
   - ☐ Wright's plane hopped across the sky.
   - ☐ The small hen laid eight to ten eggs a day for a week.
   - ☐ The people of Kitty Hawk eke out a bare existence.

9. Look at the word *stinging* in the second paragraph. What does this word mean? How does this compare to a bee's sting?

   _____

   _____

   _____

   _____

   _____

10. Which sentences best describe the importance of the event?
    - ☐ The course of the flight up and down was exceedingly erratic, partly due to the irregularity of the air, and partly to lack of experience in handling this machine. The control of the front rudder was difficult because it is balanced too close to the center.
    - ☐ The velocity of the wind was over 35 feet per second. The speed of the machine over the ground against this wind was ten feet per second. The speed of the machine relative to the air was over 45 feet per second, and the length of the flight was equivalent to a flight of 540 feet made in calm air.
    - ☐ This flight lasted only 12 seconds, but it was nevertheless the first in the history of the world in which a machine carrying a man had raised itself by its own power into the air in full flight, had sailed forward without reduction of speed and had finally landed at a point as high as that from which it started.
    - ☐ Ward, having just seen a piece of machinery lift itself from the ground and fly, a thing at that time considered as impossible as perpetual motion, was ready to believe nearly anything. But after going out and having a good look at the wonderful fowl, he returned with the remark, "It's only a common looking chicken!"

Name   Date

ⓐ Narrative Writing

Narrative Writing

✔ Narrative writing tells a story. The story has a beginning, a middle and an end.

Writing Prompt

▪ Draw a picture and write a paragraph to summarize the main ideas of the fragment of *How We Made The First Flight*, by Orville Wright.

Before Writing: Write the main ideas on the mind map.

After Writing: Use the writing checklist. Read your story to a partner.

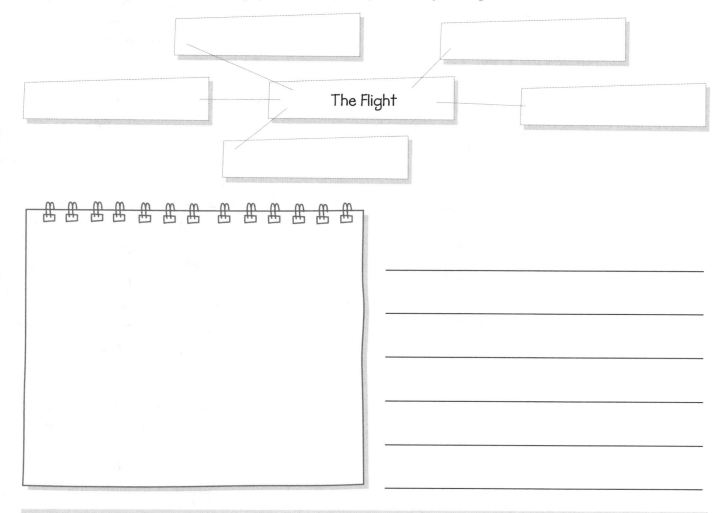

The Flight

ELD Standard
    Write narratives that describe the setting, characters, and events.
ELA Standard
    Write responses to literature. Demonstrate an understanding of a literary work.

Name _____   Date _____

ⓐ Subject–Verb Agreement

Subject–Verb Agreement

✔ The verb must <u>agree</u> with the subject of a sentence.

If the subject of a sentence is a singular noun, or *he*, *she* or *it*, the verb must be singular.

He <u>uses</u> the telescope.

If the subject of a sentence is a plural noun, or *I*, *we*, *you* or *they*, the verb must be plural.

The windstorms <u>occur</u> when hot air hits cold, dry air.

Rule   If the subject ends in <u>s</u>, the verb can't end in <u>s</u>.

The <u>boys look</u> through the telescope.

If the verb ends in <u>s</u>, then the subject can't end in <u>s</u>.

The <u>boy looks</u> through the telescope.

Exception   Watch for singular nouns that end in <u>s</u>.

<u>Glass</u> covers the telescope's eyepiece.

▪ Underline the correct verb in each sentence.

▪ Read the sentences to a partner.

1. The telescope (work, works) by gathering light sent from a distant object that is too faint to see with the eye alone.

2. Factories (make, makes) telescopes from two special pieces of glass called lenses.

3. The girl (see, sees) the image through the small lens of the telescope.

4. The scientist (study, studies) objects in space.

5. Astronauts (use, uses) telescopes to help them learn more about the universe.

6. The Hubble Space Telescope (orbit, orbits) the earth.

7. The man (wonder, wonders) at all the stars in the sky as he looks through the telescope.

8. The telescope lens (magnify, magnifies) objects in space.

9. Several people (point, points) their telescopes toward the moon.

10. They (observe, observes) the moon, stars and planets through a telescope.

ELD Standard
    Use correct parts of speech, including subject/verb agreement.
ELA Standard
    Identify and correctly use verbs, modifiers, and pronouns.

205

Name _____   Date _____

a Prefixes

■ Read the passage. Note that the prefixes in words are underlined.

The Printing Press

Before the invention of the printing press books were written and <u>re</u>written by hand. The first printing was done in China 1,500 years ago. Words were carved into a block of wood. The blocks were then inked and <u>re</u>inked and pressed against wet paper. It was almost 1,000 years before this method was <u>re</u>placed and finally <u>dis</u>appeared.

Johannes Guttenberg <u>un</u>locked the key to printing. He worked <u>non</u>stop to design moveable type. He printed the first book in 1456. He printed the Bible. He thought it was <u>im</u>proper to print any other book as his first book. Guttenberg's moveable type method made it possible to print and <u>re</u>print more books than ever before.

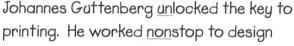

✔ The parts of the underlined words in "The Printing Press" are prefixes.

✔ Prefixes are put in front of a root word.

inked ⟶ <u>re</u>inked   proper ⟶ <u>im</u>proper

appeared ⟶ <u>dis</u>appeared   placed ⟶ <u>re</u>placed

locked ⟶ <u>un</u>locked

✔ Prefixes change the meaning of a word.

appear changes to <u>dis</u>appear (*not appear*)

ELD Standard
Spell correctly roots, inflections, suffixes, prefixes, and syllable constructions.
ELA Standard
Spell roots, suffixes, prefixes, contractions, and syllable constructions correctly.

✔ A prefix is a part of a word added to the beginning of a root word.
A prefix changes the meaning of the root word.

Prefix	Meaning	Example
dis	not, opposite of	disappear (not appear)
im	not, without	improper (not proper)
in	not, without	incapable (not capable)
un	not, opposite of	untie (not tied)
non	not, opposite of, without	nonstop (without stops)
mis	incorrectly	mismanage (incorrectly manage)
pre	before	preread (read before)
re	again, back	replace (place again)

■ Look at the prefixes in the table above. Write the meaning of each prefix in the table below.

■ Use each word in a sentence. Read your sentences to a partner.

Word	Meaning of Prefix	Sentence
disappear		
improper		
incapable		
untied		
nonstop		
mismanage		
preread		
replace		

207

Name _____   Date _____

a Demonstrating Comprehension

- Read the advertisement to a partner.
- Answer the questions together.

Introducing Animal Mania
An Exciting New Computer Game for Animal Lovers

Do you like animals? Do you like wild animals like tigers and lions and domesticated animals like dogs and cats? This computer game takes you on a trip around the world to see the most <u>fascinating</u> animals.

Animal Mania is a game that shows you 200 color photographs of animals from around the world. Your goal is to guess the habitat where the animal lives. Does the animal live in a forest, a jungle, an ocean or in someone's backyard? The more animals you match to their habitats, the more points you earn. The goal of the game is to earn 200 points.

Now, for a limited time only, you can receive a free Animal Mania poster with ten animals that are featured in the game by logging on to the Animal Mania website on the Internet, www.AnimaliaMania.com, and completing the coupon like the one below.

Name _____

Address _____

City _____

State _____ Zip Code _____

Order Today!
Allow 4 – 6 weeks for delivery.

ELD Standard
Describe main ideas and supporting details of a text.
ELA Standard
Read aloud narrative and expository text fluently and accurately and with appropriate pacing, intonation, and expression.

1. The object of the game is to —
   - [ ] learn the names of jungle animals
   - [ ] match the animals to their habitats
   - [ ] label animals big or small
   - [ ] identify the country where the animals live

2. All of these are required on the coupon <u>except</u> —
   - [ ] address
   - [ ] name
   - [ ] zip code
   - [ ] phone number

3. To get a free poster you must —
   - [ ] log on to the Animal Mania website
   - [ ] request it on a piece of paper
   - [ ] log on to www.Animal
   - [ ] send your credit card number

4. When you play this game you will learn mainly about —
   - [ ] cats
   - [ ] travel
   - [ ] dogs
   - [ ] animals

5. How long will it take to get the Animal Mania poster?
   - [ ] three to four days
   - [ ] one to two weeks
   - [ ] five to six weeks
   - [ ] four to six weeks

6. Why do businesses advertise?
   - [ ] to convince you to buy their products
   - [ ] to describe a new product that you might want
   - [ ] to inform you about something new on the market
   - [ ] All of the above.

7. What is an antonym of *fascinating*?
   - [ ] sleepy
   - [ ] exciting
   - [ ] interesting
   - [ ] boring

8. What <u>don't</u> you need to play the game?
   - [ ] a monitor
   - [ ] a keyboard
   - [ ] books
   - [ ] electricity

Name   Date

b Descriptive Writing

✔ Descriptive writing tells how something looks, smells, sounds, tastes and feels.

Writing Prompt

■ Draw a picture of an animal. Write a paragraph to describe the animal, what it eats and the habitat where the animal lives.
Have a partner read your paragraph and revise your writing.

_____

_____

_____

_____

ELD Standard
     Begin to use a variety of genres in writing.
ELA Standard
     Edit and revise manuscripts to improve the meaning and focus of writing.

Name _____   Date _____

a Interpreting Charts

National Holidays

Two types of holidays are state holidays and national holidays. Arbor Day became a state holiday in Nebraska when lawmakers there decided the state would celebrate it each year. Other states celebrate Arbor Day, too. In the United States, each state can choose different holidays that its citizens will celebrate.

Some holidays are celebrated by every state in our country. These types of holidays, which are legislated by the national government to honor our country and its people, are called national holidays. The chart below shows some of the national holidays that we celebrate.

Holiday	Date	What We Honor
Martin Luther King, Jr. Day	Third Monday in January	Martin L. King's birthday
President's Day	Third Monday in February	George Washington's and Abraham Lincoln's birthdays
Memorial Day	Last Monday in May	U.S. soldiers killed in war
Independence Day	July 4th	Independence from England
Labor Day	First Monday in September	Working people
Columbus Day	Second Monday in October	Christopher Columbus' first landing in America
Veteran's Day	November 11th	Soldiers who fought in wars
Thanksgiving Day	Fourth Tuesday in November	Pilgrims' first harvest

Some national holidays celebrate famous events in history. On Thanksgiving Day, for example, we remember how the Pilgrims thanked God for their harvest and celebrated with the Native Americans who had helped them.

ELD Standard
Read and orally identify text features such as title, table of contents, chapter headings, diagrams, charts, glossaries, and indexes.
ELA Standard
Understand how text features (e.g., format, graphics, sequences, diagrams, illustrations, charts, maps) make information accessible and usable.

On Independence Day, we remember July 4th, 1776—the day early leaders of America declared that the United States was free from England. Today, on July 4th, we also celebrate the freedom that American citizens have. Each year, new citizens join the United States to enjoy the freedom granted to the people in our country.

Two of our national holidays honor well-known citizens of our country. We honor George Washington and Abraham Lincoln on President's Day. On Martin Luther King, Jr. Day we remember the man who fought for the freedom of all people.

Some national holidays honor groups of our citizens. On Labor Day we honor all people who work, or labor, to provide things we need. On Veteran's Day we remember Americans who have fought to keep our country free. Memorial Day is a holiday in which we remember soldiers who have died during wars. All of these holidays celebrate important events or people in American history.

1. In which month do we celebrate Martin Luther King, Jr. Day?
   - [ ] January
   - [ ] February
   - [ ] March
   - [ ] April

2. Where do you think you can find more information about national holidays?
   - [ ] in a science book
   - [ ] in a history book
   - [ ] on a museum's website
   - [ ] in a phone book

3. This chart does not tell you —
   - [ ] the date of each national holiday
   - [ ] the name of each holiday
   - [ ] what or who we honor on each day
   - [ ] events that will take place on each national holiday

4. This chart was written in order to —
   - [ ] list the dates of national holidays
   - [ ] sell tickets to events
   - [ ] persuade people to celebrate national holidays
   - [ ] advertise Martin Luther King, Jr. Day

5. Who do we honor on Labor Day?
   - ☐ Americans who fought in wars
   - ☐ President Lincoln and President Washington
   - ☐ all people who work
   - ☐ the Pilgrims

6. Which of these is an opinion?
   - ☐ Columbus Day comes once a year.
   - ☐ Thanksgiving is the fourth Thursday in November.
   - ☐ Two of our national holidays honor well-known citizens of our country.
   - ☐ These are the best holidays in the world.

7. What is another possible title for this selection?
   - ☐ Days We Celebrate in the U.S.A.
   - ☐ The Reasons We Celebrate Thanksgiving
   - ☐ Hurray for Labor Day
   - ☐ State Holidays and Their Meanings

8. What word best describes this passage?
   - ☐ exciting
   - ☐ informative
   - ☐ sacred
   - ☐ descriptive

■ Write a summary of this article.

_____

_____

_____

_____

_____

_____

213

Name   Date

ⓐ Informative Writing

✔ Informative writing gives you facts about something. It gives readers a close up view.
  It sometimes show differences and similarities between two events.

Writing Prompt

▪ Explain the differences in the way we celebrate two national holidays—Independence Day
  and Thanksgiving.

▪ Write facts about the two holidays in a summary and draw a picture to represent each one.

Before Writing: Complete the Venn Diagram on page 215.
                 List the differences between the holidays.
                 List the similarities between the holidays.

After Writing: Use the writing checklist at the back of the book.
                 Read your description to a partner.

ELD Standard
    Begin to use a variety of genres in writing.
ELA Standard
    Create multi-paragraph expository compositions.

How the Celebrations Are Alike

The Way We Celebrate
Independence Day

1.

2.

3.

4.

1.

2.

3.

4.

The Way We Celebrate
Thanksgiving

1.

2.

3.

4.

Name   Date

a Appositives

━━ ━━ ━ ━━ ━ ━━ ━ ━━ ━ ━ ━━ ━ ━━ ━ ━━ ━ ━━ ━ ━━ ━ ━━ ━ ━━

Appositives

✔ An <u>appositive</u> follows a noun or pronoun to *explain* or *identify* the noun or pronoun.

Mrs. Garcia, my cousin, lived on a ranch.

My cousin is an appositive. It <u>identifies</u> Mrs. Garcia.

The Potomac, one of the longest rivers in the eastern U.S., flows past Mount Vernon.

One of the longest rivers in the eastern U.S. is an appositive. It <u>explains</u> what The Potomac is.

✔ An explanatory word or phrase that follows a noun or pronoun is an <u>appositive</u>.
There are usually commas around the appositive.

━━ ━━ ━ ━━ ━ ━━ ━ ━━ ━ ━ ━━ ━ ━━ ━ ━━ ━ ━━ ━ ━━ ━ ━━ ━ ━━

▪ Underline the appositive in these sentences.

▪ Read the sentences to a partner.

1. George Washington, the first president of the United States, was born on February 22, 1732.

2. A war for independence, the Revolutionary War, broke out in 1776.

3. George Washington, a general, led the troops during the Revolutionary War.

4. George Washington's farm, Mount Vernon, still exists today.

5. President's Day, the third Monday in February, honors George Washington.

6. The Revolutionary War, a war for independence, was fought by George Washington's troops against the British.

7. George Washington, our first president, served from 1789–1797.

8. Washington Avenue, our town's main street, was named after George Washington.

9. The father of our nation, George Washington, became a surveyor when he was a teenager.

10. Virginia, one of the richest of the 13 colonies, was George Washington's birthplace.

ELD Standard
Use correct parts of speech, including subject–verb agreement.
ELA Standard
Identify and correctly use prepositional phrases, appositives and independent and dependent clauses.

■ Use the following as appositives in sentences.

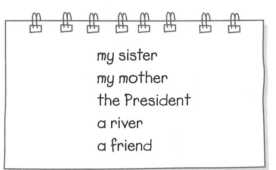

my sister
my mother
the President
a river
a friend

1. _____

_____

2. _____

_____

3. _____

_____

4. _____

_____

5. _____

_____

Name

Date

ⓐ Describing Main Ideas

- Read the questions on page 219 first.
- Read the passage to a partner. Your partner *sums up* the main idea after each paragraph. Switch roles.
- Answer the questions.

Abraham Lincoln

In 1809, Abraham Lincoln was born in Kentucky in a log cabin. He was given the nickname "Abe" shortly after he was born. Abraham and his family moved from Kentucky to Indiana. Sadly, Abraham's mother died when he was nine years old, but he grew up to be wise, tall and strong. He loved to wrestle and tell stories. Though he only went to school for one year, Abe was very intelligent and learned to read on his own. Abe grew up, worked hard and helped his neighbors. One time, he earned money taking a load of produce down the Mississippi River to New Orleans. This was the first time Abe saw slaves.

In 1830, the Lincolns moved to Illinois. After Abe left home, he had many jobs. At one time, he was a storekeeper and later he became a postmaster, but what Abe really wanted was to become a lawyer. He read books about the law and studied, and in 1836, Abe passed the test to become a lawyer.

Abraham Lincoln decided to go into politics. In 1860 he was elected President of the United States. President Lincoln became one of our greatest presidents. He led the United States in the Civil War. He was also a great orator. He is remembered as the president who <u>freed</u> the slaves. Abraham Lincoln was truly a self-made man. When he was assassinated in a theater in 1865, it was a great loss for America. We celebrate Abraham Lincoln's birthday on President's Day.

ELD Standard
  Describe main ideas and supporting details in text.
ELA Standard
  Discern main ideas and concepts presented in texts, identifying and assessing evidence that supports those ideas.

1. The main idea of this story is that —
   - [ ] Lincoln came from modest means who became one of our greatest presidents
   - [ ] Lincoln was killed in 1865 in a theater
   - [ ] Lincoln became a famous lawyer who was against slavery
   - [ ] Lincoln went into politics to help his neighbors

2. Lincoln worked as all of the following <u>except</u> —
   - [ ] a wrestler
   - [ ] a storekeeper
   - [ ] a postmaster
   - [ ] a lawyer

3. In 1860, Lincoln became —
   - [ ] a lawyer after he studied hard
   - [ ] President of the United States
   - [ ] a famous school teacher in Illinois
   - [ ] a farmer and a great orator

4. Abe Lincoln probably thought the most important thing he did was —
   - [ ] free the slaves
   - [ ] leave Kentucky
   - [ ] become a lawyer
   - [ ] attend school

5. In this story, <u>freed</u> means —
   - [ ] financed
   - [ ] let go
   - [ ] fought
   - [ ] ran

6. Another good title for this story is —
   - [ ] The Wrestler
   - [ ] The Postmaster
   - [ ] A Great President
   - [ ] Mississippi

7. At the end of this story, you learned why Lincoln was considered —
   - [ ] a great president
   - [ ] a wrestler
   - [ ] a worker
   - [ ] a news broadcaster

8. This article is most like —
   - [ ] a folktale
   - [ ] historical fiction
   - [ ] a biography
   - [ ] an adventure story

9. What event in Lincoln's life might have influenced his views on slavery?
   - [ ] The death of his mother
   - [ ] Seeing a slave market for the first time
   - [ ] Getting elected as president of the United States
   - [ ] Becoming a lawyer and fighting for people's rights

Name   Date

ᵇ Writing a Summary

Writing Prompt

▪ Write a summary of this passage on Abraham Lincoln. Write the main idea of each paragraph. Write the important details.

Before Writing: Complete the main idea map below.

After Writing: Use the writing checklist at the back of the book.
Ask a partner to use the writing checklist to edit your writing.
Read your summary to a partner.

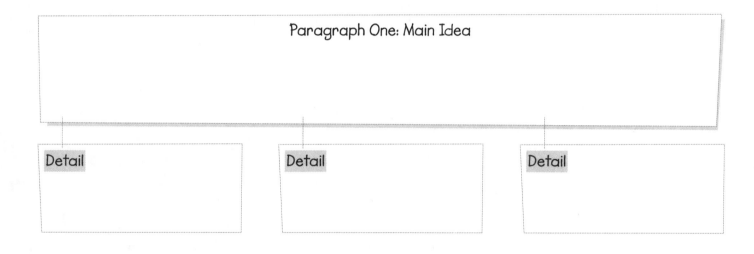

Paragraph One: Main Idea

Detail

Detail

Detail

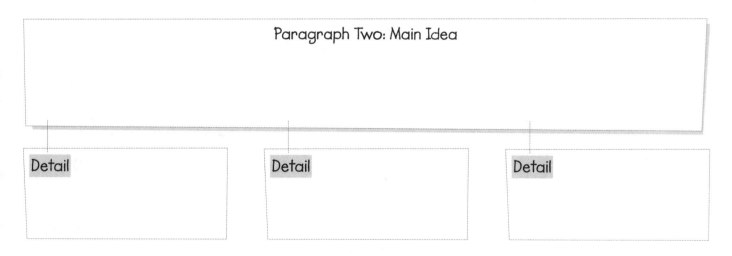

Paragraph Two: Main Idea

Detail

Detail

Detail

ELD Standard
Write short narrative stories.
ELA Standard
Complete multiple paragraph narrative compositions.

Paragraph Three: Main Idea

Detail

Detail

Detail

Summary

_____

_____

_____

_____

_____

_____

_____

_____

Name _____   Date _____

a Demonstrating Comprehension

Fresh Pumpkin Pie

This is the most delicious pie for Thanksgiving dinner!

Baking time needed: 25–30 minutes

You will need:

- 1 cup fresh pumpkin, peeled, seeded and cubed
- $1/2$ cup sugar
- $1/4$ teaspoon cinnamon
- 2 pre-made pie crusts
- A sharp knife and a fork

1. Preheat the oven to 350°F.
2. Peel the skin off the pumpkin and remove the pulp and seeds from inside.
3. Cut the pumpkin into 1-inch cubes with a sharp knife.
4. Place one of the pie crusts in the bottom of a pie pan.
5. Put the pieces of pumpkin on top of the bottom pie crust.
6. Mix the cinnamon and sugar together and sprinkle over the pumpkin.
7. Put the second pie crust on top of the pumpkin.
8. Mold the pie crust edges to the pie pan with a fork.
9. Slit holes in the top of the piecrust with the knife.
10. Bake the pie in the oven at 350°F for 25–30 minutes.

1. When you make a pumpkin pie, the knife is used to —
   - ☐ carve the pumpkin into a jack-o-lantern
   - ☐ stir the sugar
   - ☐ cut the pumpkin into several 1-inch cubes
   - ☐ cut the pumpkin off the vine

2. A pumpkin pie is most like —
   - ☐ a vanilla milkshake
   - ☐ a chocolate cream pie
   - ☐ a sweet potato pie
   - ☐ a carrot cake

3. After you set the oven to 350°, you should —
   - ☐ cut the pumpkin into 1-inch cubes
   - ☐ put the pieces of pumpkin into the bottom pie crust
   - ☐ slit holes on the top of the pie crust
   - ☐ peel the skin off of the pumpkin

4. This is an opinion in the recipe.
   - ☐ Baking time is 25–30 minutes.
   - ☐ You will need $1/2$ cup of sugar and a $1/4$ teaspoon of cinnamon.
   - ☐ Set the oven to 350°F.
   - ☐ This is the most delicious pie for Thanksgiving dinner!

5. According to the recipe, the last thing you do is —
   - ☐ cut the pumpkin
   - ☐ mold the pie crust edges
   - ☐ bake the pie in the oven at 350°
   - ☐ eat the pie with your family

6. What is the best way to find out more about baking pies?
   - ☐ read a cookbook
   - ☐ make a cake
   - ☐ have a party
   - ☐ look for pie recipes in a history book

7. What would happen to the pie if you baked it for 60 minutes?
   - ☐ the pie would burn
   - ☐ the pie would be dry
   - ☐ the pie would taste more delicious
   - ☐ the pie would be cold

8. Why do you think pumpkin pie has been so popular on Thanksgiving since the time of the Pilgrims?
   - ☐ because pumpkin tastes good with turkey
   - ☐ because pumpkin pie is easy to prepare
   - ☐ because pumpkins are in season and are plentiful
   - ☐ because people do not use all the pumpkins at Halloween

ELD Standard
   Read and orally identify examples of fact/opinion and cause/effect in literature and content area texts.
ELA Standard
   Distinguish facts, supported inferences, and opinions in text.

Name   Date

b Expository Writing

✔ Expository writing gives directions on how to do or make something.

Writing Prompt

■ Write and illustrate the directions for making a fresh strawberry ice cream sundae.

Before Writing: Think about the ingredients and steps needed for making the sundae.

After Writing: Use the writing checklist at the back of the book.
Read the directions to a partner.

Fresh Strawberry Ice Cream Sundae

You will need:
■
■
■
■

Steps:

1.

2.

3.

4.

5.

6.

Fresh Strawberry
Ice Cream Sundae

ELD Standard
Begin to use a variety of genres in writing.
ELA Standard
Create multi-paragraph expository compositions.

Name _____   Date _____

ⓐ Demonstrating Comprehension

▪ Read the questions on page 226 first.

▪ Read the passage to a partner. Your partner *sums up* the main idea after each paragraph. Switch roles.

▪ Answer the questions.

Martin Luther King, Jr.
"I have a dream!"

Why do we celebrate Martin Luther King Day on January 15th? Who was this man who changed history for African-Americans?

Martin Luther King, Jr. spent his life trying to get equal rights for African-Americans. When Martin was a child in Atlanta, Georgia, African-Americans had to sit at the back of the bus. They had to go to different schools, sit in different areas in the movie theaters, and even use separate restrooms. African-Americans were segregated in all aspects of life. This separation of African-Americans was called "segregation."

Martin first learned about segregation when he was six. Two of his best friends were white boys. Martin played with them every day. However, when the boys became old enough to go to school, the two friends went to a different school than Martin. Martin had to attend a school for African-Americans.

In spite of the problems of African-Americans when Martin was growing up, he had a happy childhood. His father was a Baptist minister and his mother was a school teacher. They lived in a twelve-room house in a very nice neighborhood. As Martin got older, he learned that many African-Americans were not as fortunate as he was.

In high school, Martin was a good student. He was very articulate. Sometimes, his friends would tease him because he used such big words. Martin graduated from high school at age fifteen and went on to college. He became a minister and started his long struggle to make life better for African-Americans. He wanted African-Americans to have the basic civil rights such as the right to vote, the right to have good jobs and the right to have a good education. He also wanted segregation to end.

ELD Standard
    Describe main ideas and supporting details of a text.
ELA Standard
    Discern main ideas and concepts presented in texts, identifying and assessing evidence that supports those ideas.

Martin Luther King, Jr. believed that changes should come about in a peaceful way. He organized peaceful marches and demonstrations. He traveled around the country organizing African-Americans. King was a great orator. His most famous speech was entitled, "I Have A Dream". In the speech, he said, *"I have a dream that my four little children will one day live in a nation where they will not be judged by the color of their skin but by the content of their character."* Martin Luther King, Jr. accomplished much before he was assassinated in 1968.

1. What did Martin Luther King, Jr. do to help African-Americans?
   - [ ] He became a famous author.
   - [ ] He became an engineer.
   - [ ] He fought to end segregation and for civil rights.
   - [ ] He started his own university.

2. There is enough information in this article to show that —
   - [ ] African-Americans owned many businesses
   - [ ] African-Americans never rode on buses
   - [ ] African-Americans were segregated
   - [ ] African-Americans went to good schools

3. If you wanted to know more about Martin Luther King, Jr. you should —
   - [ ] read a history book
   - [ ] look on the internet under ministers
   - [ ] read a science book
   - [ ] look on an Atlanta, Georgia map

4. The words in quotation marks at the beginning of the article were first spoken by —
   - [ ] George Washington
   - [ ] Martin Luther King, Jr.
   - [ ] King George V
   - [ ] Thomas Jefferson

5. Another good name for this article is —
   - [ ] An American Hero: Martin Luther King, Jr.
   - [ ] An American Architect: Martin Luther King, Jr.
   - [ ] The Great High School
   - [ ] The Bus Ride

6. Which of these sentences would fit best at the end of this article?
   - [ ] Martin Luther King, Jr. lived in Atlanta, Georgia.
   - [ ] Martin Luther King, Jr. became a minister and started a long struggle to make life better for everyone.
   - [ ] Martin Luther King, Jr. liked to travel.
   - [ ] Martin Luther King, Jr. is honored today by a special holiday for helping to make his dream come true.

Name _____   Date _____

b Narrative Writing

Narrative Writing

✔ Narrative writing tells a story.

It has a beginning, a middle and an end.

Writing Prompt

■ On a separate sheet of paper, write a summary of this article on Martin Luther King, Jr. Start your summary below.

Before Writing: Complete the main idea map, listing the most significant details of Martin Luther King Jr.'s life.

After Writing: Use the writing checklist at the back of the book.
Have a partner recheck or edit your writing using the writing checklist.
Read your summary to a partner.

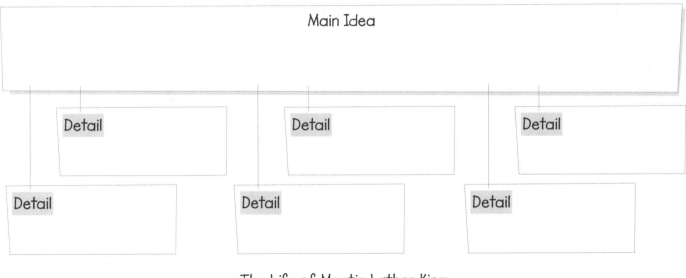

The Life of Martin Luther King

_____

_____

_____

ELD Standard
    Write narrative stories.
ELA Standard
    Complete multi-paragraph narrative compositions.

Name _____   Date _____

⒜ Quotations

━ ━

Use of Quotation Marks

✔ To enclose a direct quotation of what someone said.

Maria said, "Memorial Day is at the end of May."

"Memorial Day is to honor Civil War soldiers," explained the teacher.

✔ To enclose each part of a divided quotation.

"Isn't it too bad," said John, "that we can't go to the Memorial Day Parade?"

✔ When referring to the name of a book, poem or play.

I have read "The History of Memorial Day" five times.

━ ━

▪ Rewrite each sentence putting in the quotation marks.

▪ Read the sentences with quotations to a partner.

1. The teacher said, Memorial Day was begun in 1868 by a group of women in Pennsylvania.

   _____

   _____

2. Memorial Day was to remember those who died fighting the Civil War, explained Tom.

   _____

   _____

3. Our town has a parade on Memorial Day, said Ricardo.

   _____

   _____

ELD Standard
Edit writing for basic conventions.

ELA Standard
Use a colon to separate hours and minutes and to introduce a list; use quotation marks around the exact words of a speaker and titles of poems, songs, short stories, and so forth.

4. Shao asked, Where are the Civil War veterans buried?

_____

5. Mike said, Memorial Day is held on the last Monday in May.

_____

6. Isn't it too bad, said Gina, that we can't go to the Memorial Day Parade this year?

_____

_____

7. Grandfather said, Memorial Day was originally known as Decoration Day.

_____

_____

8. Aren't they the ones, asked Jason, that are going to put the flowers on the veterans' graves?

_____

_____

9. The book that tells about the history of Memorial Day is Famous American Holidays.

_____

_____

10. Have you read the poem Memorial Day Veterans?

_____

Name _____   Date _____

ⓐ Identifying and Correctly Using Verbs

- Read about often-misused verbs below.
- Think about how to correctly use the verbs *sit* and *set*.

Sit, Sat, Sitting

Sit means the physical act of sitting down.

- ✔ *They <u>sit</u> near the front.*
- ✔ *Where is he <u>sitting</u>?*
- ✔ *They <u>sat</u> near the teacher.*
- ✔ *The girls <u>sat</u> here yesterday morning.*

Set, Set, Setting

Set means to put something down or to establish something.

- ✔ *Please <u>set</u> that down.*
- ✔ *Where have you <u>set</u> the book?*
- ✔ *Is he <u>setting</u> the table?*
- ✔ *In the bicycle race last week, the leader <u>set</u> the pace.*

- Use the correct form of the verbs *sit* or *set* from the notepad in each sentence.
- Read the sentences to a partner.

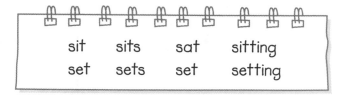

| sit | sits | sat | sitting |
| set | sets | set | setting |

1. Won't you _____ that book on Veteran's Day down on the table?

2. Did he _____ the flag here?

ELD Standard
   Use correct parts of speech.
ELA Standard
   Identify and correctly use verbs that are often misused (e.g., lie/lay, sit/sat, rise/raise), modifiers, and pronouns.

3. She had _____ the wreath there first.

4. The government _____ November 11th as the day to commemorate Veterans Day.

5. The day began when an armistice was _____ in place at the end of World War I in 1918.

6. No one knows who is _____ behind the President of the United States.

7. They _____ on the front bleachers to watch the Veteran's Day Parade.

8. We have _____ here all morning to watch the Veteran's Day Parade.

9. Where did he _____ the tickets to the game?

10. Many people _____ a flag on their cars during the Veteran's Day Parade.

11. Was she _____ with the veteran's from the Vietnam War on Veteran's Day?

12. How long did she _____ next to the Tomb of the Unknowns?

13. The military general _____ next to the president of the United States.

14. The general's horse _____ the pace during the Veteran's Day Parade.

15. Where are the World War II veterans _____?

Name _____   Date _____

a Interpreting Charts

25th Annual County Fair and Labor Day Activities
Schedule of Events
County Fairgrounds
August 28th – September 4th

Animal Events

August 28 – 2:00 P.M.	Swine Racing Contest
August 30 – 3:00 P.M.	Cow Milking Contest
September 3 – 2:00 P.M.	Sheep Shearing Exhibition

Music Events

September 1 – 7:00 P.M.	Rock and Roll Band
September 2 – 8:00 P.M.	Country Music
September 4 – 6:00 P.M.	Rap Contest

Cooking Events

August 28 – 2:00 P.M.	Pie-Eating Contest
August 29 – 4:00 P.M.	Chili Cook-Off
September 3 – 5:00 P.M.	Cook-out

Gardening Events

September 1 – 5:00 P.M.	Biggest Tomato Contest
September 2 – 3:00 P.M.	Gardening Techniques Lecture
September 4 – 1:00 P.M.	The Garden Doctor: Questions and Answers

1. Where will the County Fair be held?
   ☐ county school grounds
   ☐ county park
   ☐ Exposition Hall
   ☐ county fairground

2. When will the County Fair be held?
   ☐ August 26 – September 3
   ☐ August 28 – September 4
   ☐ August 27 – September 3
   ☐ August 27 – August 29

3. What two events are happening on the same day at the same time?
   ☐ the rap contest and the sheep shearing exhibition
   ☐ the swine racing contest and the pie-eating contest
   ☐ the cook-out and the cow milking contest
   ☐ the garden doctor and the country music

4. Which events need musical instruments?
   ☐ animal events
   ☐ gardening events
   ☐ cooking events
   ☐ music events

5. If you don't stay until 6:00 P.M. on September 4th, you'll miss the —
   ☐ barbecue
   ☐ sheep shearing
   ☐ garden doctor
   ☐ rap contest

6. There is enough information in this schedule to show that —
   ☐ there are lots of things to do at the county fair
   ☐ there are 100 pies in the pie-eating contest
   ☐ the chili cook-off has only spicy chili
   ☐ only boys can enter the rap contest

7. The county fair has been happening for —
   ☐ 5 years
   ☐ 10 years
   ☐ 25 years
   ☐ 30 years

8. What would cause the September 3rd events to be cancelled?
   ☐ a parade
   ☐ another county fair
   ☐ biggest lettuce contest
   ☐ rain

ELD Standard
Read and orally identify text features such as title, table of contents, chapter headings, diagrams, charts, glossaries, and indexes in written text.

ELA Standard
Understand how text features (e.g., format, graphics, sequences, diagrams, illustrations, charts, maps) make information accessible and usable.

Name _____   Date _____

a Suffixes

✔ A <u>suffix</u> is a word part that is added to the end of a root word.

✔ A suffix changes the meaning of the root word.

Suffix	Meaning	Example
-ly	in the manner of	*quickly* (in a quick manner)
-er	one who does	*teacher* (one who teaches)
-ful	full of	*careful* (full of care)
-less	without	*treeless* (without trees)

▪ Underline the word with the suffix in each sentence. Read the sentences to a partner.

1. The wedding planner helped her plan her wedding celebration.

2. You must be careful to send invitations to all of his friends.

3. The balloons flew swiftly to the treetops.

4. The music played loudly at the festival.

5. The groom was thoughtless in forgetting the bride's mother's name.

▪ Use each word in a sentence. Read your sentences to a partner.

1. planner _____

2. thoughtless _____

3. painter _____

4. careful _____

5. loudly _____

ELD Standard
    Spell correctly roots, inflections, suffixes, prefixes, and syllable constructions.
ELA Standard
    Spell roots, suffixes, prefixes, contractions, and syllable constructions correctly.

Name _____   Date _____

a Writing a Narrative Essay

United States of America
A Mosaic of Diversity

Some people think that the United States is a melting pot. This means that people from various nations around the world, such as Mexico, France, Pakistan, and China, blend into the United States and become assimilated quickly. Other people speak of the United States as a mosaic of different people who come from many countries. Each group of people maintain the customs of their land of origin.

In reality, the United States is both a melting pot and a mosaic. The United States is a land of many cultures, religions and languages. It is a pluralistic society. "Pluralistic" means that many cultures, religions and languages exist in America. Yet, the people from all these cultures come together as United States citizens and share the same country and flag, along with the English language, and ideals for freedom and the desire to progress.

■ Fill out the chart below.

List some of the countries from which Americans originally came from.
List some of the languages that are spoken in the United States.
List how people from diverse countries are alike as U.S. citizens.

	Differences (Mosaic)	Similarities (Melting Pot)
Countries	1. 2. 3. 4.	1. 2. 3. 4. 5. 6. 7. 8.
Languages	1. 2. 3. 4.	

Writing Prompt

- Use the information in the chart to write a narrative about diversity in America from a specific point of view. Choose one of the following points of view and support it with facts and opinions.

Point of View #1

Differences in cultures and languages allow the United States to prosper.

Point of View #2

The United States would be a better place if everyone came from the same country and spoke the same language.

Before Writing: Use the information on your chart to help you think of facts and opinions that support your point of view.

Brainstorm other facts to support your point of view on the lines below.

After Writing: Use the writing checklist at the back of the book to edit your work.

Read your narrative on diversity to a partner.

_____

_____

_____

_____

_____

236

ELD Standard

Use models to write about narratives.

ELA Standard

Write narratives. Establish a point of view.

Name _____ Date _____

ⓐ Using the Pronouns *I* and *Me*

- -

Using the Pronouns *I* and *Me*

✔ Use *I* as a subject of a sentence and after a form of the verb *to be*. Always capitalize *I*.

I know about the Bill of Rights.

The guilty party was I.

✔ Place *I* last in compound subjects.

Mark and I read the Bill of Rights.

✔ Use *me* after prepositions such as *for, at, with* and *to*.

Dad went with me to the United States Congress.

✔ Place *me* last in a compound noun that follows an action verb and after words such as *for, at, of, with* and *to*.

The teacher told Carlos and me to read last.

My mom gave a dollar to Lisa and me.

- -

▪ Write the correct pronoun (*I* or *me*) in each sentence.

▪ Read the sentences to a partner.

1. The teacher read the Bill of Rights to Ricardo and _____.

2. Maria and _____ knew that the Bill of Rights is stated in the first ten amendments to the Constitution.

3. The third amendment protects you and _____ from having to house soldiers during peacetime.

4. Carlos and _____ recited the fourth amendment which protects people and their property from searches without good reason.

5. The fifth amendment protects you and _____ from having to face trial more than once for the same crime.

ELD Standard
    Use correct parts of speech, including subject-verb agreement.
ELA Standard
    Identify and correctly use verbs that are often misused, modifiers, and pronouns.

237

6. The case went to trial. The guilty one was _____.

7. The sixth amendment guaranteed a quick trial for _____.

8. _____ know the seventh amendment guarantees a jury trial for court cases.

9. Did _____ tell you that the ninth amendment reserves for the people all rights not listed in the Constitution?

10. The Senator gave _____ a copy of the 10th amendment, which saves all other powers for the states and people.

11. Does the Constitution protect you and _____?

12. _____ believe the United States is the best country in the world.

13. I have a replica of the original Bill of Rights with _____.

14. Natasha is going to give to _____ a copy of the amendment that protects freedom of speech.

15. Miguel and _____ did a report on how the Constitution has helped America be a pluralistic society.

Name _____   Date _____

a Reasons for Using Synonyms

✔ We use synonyms to make our writing more interesting. Look at the passage below. We can make the passage more interesting by using synonyms instead of repeating the same word over and over again.

■ Read the passage to a partner. Underline the three times the word "were" appears.

■ Replace the last two instances of "were" with a synonym. Write your new sentences.

The United States is a land of many immigrants. The earliest Americans probably were from Asia. In the 17ᵗʰ century, the pilgrims were from England. Subsequent waves of generations were from Italy, Ireland, China, the Dominican Republic, and other countries. Other people had been living on the land when the United States conquered or acquired the territory. Regardless of our roots, people of all origins value tolerance and fairness that our nation upholds.

_____

_____

_____

_____

■ Draw a line to connect the synonyms in the two columns.

land	buy
subsequent	residing
living	country
conquer	region
acquire	take over
territory	future

ELD Standard
Recognize simple antonyms and synonyms in written text.
ELA Standard
Use a thesaurus to identify alternative word choices and meanings.

Name _____   Date _____

a Possessive Pronouns

▬ ▬

Possessive Pronouns

✔ A *possessive pronoun* takes the place of a *possessive noun*. It shows who or what owns something.

The book belongs to me. It's my book. It's mine.

✔ Some possessive pronouns are used before nouns: *my, your, his, her, its, our, their.*

my hair   her cape   its union

✔ Some possessive pronouns can stand alone: *mine, yours, his, hers, its, ours, theirs.*

Where is yours?   The ball is theirs.

▬ ▬

■ Read the passage to a partner.

Cesar Chavez

We are a nation of many cultures. Its members can contribute to society, regardless of disagreements among our diverse ethnic, racial, religious, economic, and linguistic groups. One such person who overcame discrimination is Cesar Chavez. He challenged society to improve a number of issues.

Cesar Chavez is most noteworthy for drawing attention to the plight of the farm worker. He organized marches and strikes to get lawmakers to pass legislation for better working conditions, health benefits and wage increases for migrant farm workers. Cesar Chavez believed people could do anything they set out to do. His motto for the farm workers association was "sí se puede." "Yes, it can be done."

ELD Standard
Use correct parts of speech, including subject-verb agreement.
ELA Standard
Identify and correctly use verbs that are often misused, modifiers, and pronouns.

■ Read the sentences about Cesar Chavez. Write the correct possessive pronouns in the blank.

1. The book entitled <u>Huelga</u> belongs to me. It's _____. (my, mine)

2. The book on Cesar Chavez tells _____ (he, his) story.

3. Cesar Chavez's family members were migrant workers. Cesar tells _____ (their, theirs) story.

4. Cesar Chavez's family followed the crops from Arizona to Northern California and back.

   _____ (Their, Theirs) life was very hard.

5. Cesar helped his family pick crops. He dropped out of school in the eighth grade to

   work and help his family. Cesar said, "It is _____ (my, mine) job to help my family."

6. For Cesar, the words "strike," "union" and "picket line," along with the struggle for social

   justice, were part of _____ (his, its) life struggle since childhood.

7. Cesar told farm workers, "You must become part of the union. _____ (Our, Ours) is a struggle for better working conditions and health benefits."

8. Cesar Chavez and Helen Chavez supported themselves by picking grapes at $1.25 per hour. Later, they helped to found the National Farm Workers Association. The motto

   sí se puede was _____ (their, theirs).

9. Cesar Chavez organized marches and strikes to get lawmakers to pass legislation for better working conditions, health benefits and wage increases for migrant farm workers

   to join the union. _____ (Its, It's) attraction was very strong.

10. The motto *sí se puede* was important to the migrant workers. "_____ (Our, Ours) workers need to know that together they can accomplish anything," said Cesar Chavez.

Name   Date

ⓐ Demonstrating Comprehension
Identifying Main Ideas

- Read the questions first on page 244.
- Read the passage to a partner. Your partner *sums up* the main idea after each paragraph. Switch roles.
- Answer the questions.

The Father of Chicano Music
"Lalo Guerrero is the first great Chicano musical artist." – Linda Ronstadt

(1) Lalo Guerrero is known as the father of Chicano music. He has written, recorded and composed hundreds of songs in a myriad of styles including bolero, ranchero, mambo, salsa and tejano. He has recorded more than twenty-five musical albums.

Lalo's Early Life

(2) Lalo Guerrero was born in 1916 in Tucson, Arizona. Lalo grew up in a very poor, predominantly Mexican area. His father was a boilermaker and fisherman and his mother was a homemaker. Lalo was one of nine children.

(3) The Guerrero family rarely ventured outside their neighborhood. They didn't have a car. The family had only a beat-up truck. The Guerrero family had no electricity in the house when Lalo was growing up. Lalo read and did his homework by a coal oil lamp. There was also no refrigerator. Lalo's mother cooked on a wood-burning stove. Lalo and his brothers and sisters took turns chopping wood for the fire.

(4) The one thing Lalo remembers about growing up was that there was always music in his house. Lalo's mother, Concepción, sang and played the guitar beautifully. It was Lalo's mother who taught him to play the guitar, chord by chord.

ELD Standard
  Describe main ideas and supporting details in text.
ELA Standard
  Discern main ideas and concepts presented in text, identifying and assessing evidence that supports those ideas.

First Compositions

(5) The first compositions Lalo wrote were primarily in Spanish but he quickly realized that there was no future for his music in the United States. Guerrero went to Mexico to try to make a name for himself. However, the Mexican music companies would not record his music because he was not born in Mexico. Lalo was Mexican-American. Eventually, some record companies bought Lalo's first musical compositions but had Mexican singers record them.

Return to the United States

(6) Lalo Guerrero returned to the United States after only six months in Mexico. "I came back very depressed to have my own people discriminate against me because I wasn't born in Mexico. It was hard to take."

Recognition

(7) In the United States, Lalo Guerrero received recognition for his social protest songs. Many of his contemporary songs are directed toward young people. Lalo's songs emphasize the importance of getting an education and they send the message to stay away from drugs and violence.

Awards and Honors

(8) Lalo Guerrero has received many honors and rewards including a Lifetime Achievement Award. But the event Lalo considered the pinnacle of his career was when he received the National Medal of the Arts in January of 1997. It was presented to him by the president of the United States.

1. How did Lalo Guerrero feel about how the Mexican recording companies treated him?

   ☐ unconcerned

   ☐ happy

   ☐ depressed

   ☐ hopeful

2. Another good name for this article is —

   ☐ Growing Up in America

   ☐ A Great Chicano Music Composer

   ☐ The Big Guitar

   ☐ A Famous Mambo

3. The words in quotation marks at the beginning of this article were spoken by —

   ☐ Cesar Chavez

   ☐ Lalo Guerrero

   ☐ Linda Ronstadt

   ☐ Lalo's mother Concepción

4. What did Lalo consider the pinnacle of his career?

   ☐ receiving a new guitar

   ☐ receiving the National Medal of the Arts

   ☐ receiving the Chicano Medal of Honor

   ☐ receiving a musical contract

5. There is enough information in this article to show that —

   ☐ Lalo Guerrero is a great musical composer

   ☐ Lalo Guerrero became very rich

   ☐ Lalo Guerrero was very happy singing in Mexico

   ☐ Lalo Guerrero was born in California

6. If you wanted to know more about Lalo Guerrero, you should —

   ☐ learn to play an instrument

   ☐ visit Arizona

   ☐ read a book about guitars

   ☐ read a book about famous Chicanos

Main Idea

✔ The main idea of a paragraph tells what the paragraph is about.
  It is a summary of the paragraph.

Writing Prompt

▪ Write two sentences stating the main idea for each paragraph in the story.

Paragraph One

_____

_____

244

Paragraph Two

_____

_____

Paragraph Three

_____

_____

Paragraph Four

_____

_____

Paragraph Five

_____

_____

Paragraph Six

_____

_____

Paragraph Seven

_____

_____

Paragraph Eight

_____

_____

Name _____   Date _____

ⓐ Reading Expository Text

✔ A food label lists the ingredients and the nutritional facts.
The purpose of the label is to tell buyers a product's contents.

▪ Read the ingredients and nutritional information on the labels below to a partner.

▪ Answer the questions with a partner.

▪ Answer the questions in complete sentences.

Mexican

Menudo
Hot and Spicy Soup
Serving size: 1 bowl

Calories	170 per serving
Calories from fat	60
Total Fat	7g
Cholesterol	30g
Sodium	20mg
Total Carbohydrates	12g
Vitamin A*	20%
Vitamin C*	2%

*Percent Daily Values (DV) are based on a 2,000 calorie diet.

Ingredients: beef tripe, water, hominy, beef broth, salt, chili pepper, sugar, corn protein

Cuban

Tostones
Fried Green Plantains
Serving size: 6 slices

Calories	120 per serving
Calories from fat	20
Cholesterol	10mg
Vitamin C*	20%

*Percent Daily Values (DV) are based on a 2,000 calorie diet.

Ingredients: plantains, corn oil, salt, preservatives

Russian

Gouryevskaya Kasha
Kasha and Fruit Pudding
Serving size: ½ cup

Calories	250 per serving
Calories from fat	220
Total Fat	24g
Total Carbohydrates	70g
Vitamin C*	10%
Vitamin A*	30%

*Percent Daily Values (DV) are based on a 2,000 calorie diet.

Ingredients: milk, cream, sugar, butter, eggs, vanilla, almonds, stewed fruit (peaches, cherries, apricot sauce)

Puerto Rican

Empanadillas
Stuffed Meat Pies
Serving size: 1 pie

Calories	150 per serving
Calories from fat	75
Total Fat	9g
Cholesterol	20mg
Sodium	8mg
Total Carbohydrates	25g
Vitamin C*	2%

*Percent Daily Values (DV) are based on a 2,000 calorie diet.

Ingredients: beef, green bell peppers, onion, garlic, tomato sauce, flour, baking soda, sugar, water, salt, vegetable oil

Chinese

Pot Stickers
Pork and Cabbage Dumplings
Serving size: 2 dumplings

Calories	200 per serving
Calories from fat	50
Total Fat	6g
Total Carbohydrates	70g
Vitamin C*	1%
Iron*	3%

*Percent Daily Values (DV) are based on a 2,000 calorie diet.

Ingredients: flour, water, salt, cabbage, ground pork

Japanese

Sushi
Rice and Fish Rolls
Serving size: 2 pieces

Calories	125 per serving
Calories from fat	8
Total Fat	1g
Total Carbohydrates	20g
Vitamin C*	10%
Vitamin A*	5%

*Percent Daily Values (DV) are based on a 2,000 calorie diet.

Ingredients: rice, seaweed, raw tuna, salt

1. What are the percents of daily value of vitamins based on in the tostones?

_____

2. How many calories are in one serving of menudo?

_____

3. How many calories in the Gouryevskaya Kasha are provided from fat?

_____

4. Which cultural food has a serving that provides 20% of the daily value of Vitamin C?

_____

5. Which cultural food has ground pork in its ingredients?

_____

6. What is the name of the food from Puerto Rico?

_____

7. Which cultural food has the fewest calories per serving?

_____

8. Which is the cultural food that is a type of soup?

_____

9. Which cultural food is made from plantains?

_____

10. Which cultural food is a dessert?

_____

ELD Standard
Use resources in the text to draw conclusions and make inferences.
ELA Standard
Read aloud narratives and expository text fluently and accurately with appropriate pacing, intonation and expression.

Name _____   Date _____

a Synonyms and Their Meanings

━━ ━━ ━━ ━━ ━━ ━━ ━━ ━━ ━━ ━━ ━━ ━━ ━━ ━━ ━━ ━━ ━━ ━━

✔ When you use a thesaurus to find synonyms, make sure you know the new word's proper meaning. This is because different words can have different connotations, or meanings.

━━ ━━ ━━ ━━ ━━ ━━ ━━ ━━ ━━ ━━ ━━ ━━ ━━ ━━ ━━ ━━ ━━ ━━

■ Find the word *thin* in a thesaurus. You might see the following:

thin   *adjective*   **synonyms**   slender, skinny, lean, slim, fine, narrow

✔ The word *thin* in the following sentence is neutral. The reader might envision a model who is not heavy.
The thin model walked down the runway during the fashion show.

✔ When we replace the word *thin* with *slender*, we change the sentence's meaning.
The slender model walked down the runway during the fashion show.
When we think of a slender model, we imagine a model who is physically attractive.

✔ If we use the word *skinny* in the same sentence, we imagine a person who is too thin.
The skinny model walked down the runway during the fashion show.
When we think of a skinny model, we imagine a model who is extremely thin.

✔ If we use the word *fine* in the same sentence, we change the meaning completely.
The fine model walked down the runway during the fashion show.
The model might have good physical characteristics or good manners.

━━ ━━ ━━ ━━ ━━ ━━ ━━ ━━ ━━ ━━ ━━ ━━ ━━ ━━ ━━ ━━ ━━ ━━

✔ To use a thesaurus, do the following:

1. Lookup the word that you want to find a synonym for.

2. Choose a word that you think is good for your needs.

3. Look up the word in the dictionary to make sure you are using it correctly.

ELD Standard
  Recognize simple antonyms and synonyms in written text. Expand recognition of and begin to use appropriately.
ELA Standard
  Use a thesaurus to identify alternative word choices and meanings.

- In each sentence, replace the underlined word with an appropriate synonym.
- Use a thesaurus to help you. Talk about your choices with a partner.
- Then rewrite the sentences.

1. The <u>old</u> couple lives in the house on the corner.

   _____

2. I saw a <u>kid</u> play baseball in the park.

   _____

3. My friend wrote a <u>skimpy</u> book report.

   _____

4. We made a <u>hasty</u> decision.

   _____

5. My <u>impatient</u> brother didn't wait for his birthday.

   _____

6. The city's lights were <u>glaring</u>.

   _____

7. My friend's sister said that Jose is very <u>pretty</u>.

   _____

Name   Date

ⓐ Interpreting Literature

- Read the questions first on page 252.
- Read the passage to a partner. Your partner *sums up* the main idea after each paragraph.
- Answer the questions.

The Creation of the World
A Chinese Myth Retold

(1) A long, long time ago, there was no sky or land in the world. There were definitely no mountains, rivers, flowers or trees. It was dark everywhere.

(2) No one knows how but an egg-shaped ball appeared on this dark world. The ball grew daily. It was like a balloon. It grew bigger and bigger. One day, after a million years or so, the large ball exploded and cracked in two.

(3) Out from the crack came a hairy giant holding a stone ax. This giant's name was Pan Koo. He had used the stone ax to chop the large ball in half. One half of the ball was pressed on top of Pan Koo's head. The other half lay underneath his feet. The weird thing was that the half on top of Pan Koo's head was slowly becoming gas. The gas softly flew upwards. Later, it became the blue, blue sky.

(4) The other half, under his feet, became the soil. It continuously sank downwards, becoming thicker and thicker. Finally, it formed itself into land. From then on, there was heaven and earth in the world.

(5) After the creation of heaven and earth, Pan Koo felt the world was a lot neater. But, he was worried that the sky and the land were so close together that they might merge again. Therefore, he used his head to hold up the sky and used his feet to solidly step on the ground. The funny thing was that his body was able to grow ten feet each day. Hence, the sky was pushed higher and higher and the land was packed down more and more solidly.

ELD Standard
Orally identify the basic sequences of events in stories.
ELA Standard
Discern main ideas and concepts presented in text, identifying and assessing evidence that supports those ideas.

(6)   This went on for eighteen thousand years. Then, Pan Koo stopped growing. By then, he had pushed the sky very far from the earth. They would never be able to merge again.

(7)   By this time, Pan Koo was already very, very old. He knew he was about to die but he didn't dare rest. He felt that the world still needed a lot of things. He decided that before he died, he was going to make the world more beautiful. For this reason, he exhaled a long breath of air. It became the spring wind and the white clouds. He called out loudly and it became the startling thunder and lightning.

(8)   He turned his hands and feet into the high mountains and hills. Then, he turned his muscles into the fertile fields. He turned his fluid blood into rivers and streams. He also turned the hair on his body into flowers, grass and trees. He made his bones and teeth into precious gems. His perspiration became the rain falling from the sky and the dew on an autumn morning. Pan Koo turned himself into so many things at once. He was so tired!

(9)   Pan Koo saw that the world he created was very beautiful. He was very satisfied. Finally, he turned his left eye into the bright sun and his right eye into the mellow moon. From then on, the sun and the moon replaced Pan Koo's eyes and shone daily on his beloved earth, mountains and streams.

(10) After Pan Koo had dedicated his precious eyes to the world, he peacefully died and left this beautiful world.

1. Why did Pan Koo use his head to hold up the sky?
   - ☐ He was worried that the sky had too many clouds and rainbows.
   - ☐ He wanted the earth to be beautiful.
   - ☐ He was afraid the sky might fall.
   - ☐ He was worried that the sky and the land were so close together that they might merge.

2. Which words in this story best describe Pan Koo?
   - ☐ a large mayor
   - ☐ a hairy giant
   - ☐ a small elf
   - ☐ a Chinese warrior

3. This story is most like —
   - ☐ a mystery
   - ☐ a myth
   - ☐ a true story
   - ☐ non-fiction

4. What is another good title for this story?
   - ☐ The Chinese Planet
   - ☐ The Big, Blue Sky
   - ☐ Pan Koo's Head Becomes Earth
   - ☐ How the Earth Was Made

5. There is enough information in this story to show that —
   - ☐ the world was created in this century
   - ☐ the creation of the world was a long process
   - ☐ it was easy to create the world
   - ☐ the sky is a mountain

6. Which words from this story show that Pan Koo was becoming gigantic?
   - ☐ His feet were solidly planted on the ground.
   - ☐ His body was able to grow ten feet each day.
   - ☐ One half of the ball was pressed on his head.
   - ☐ He was a hairy giant holding a stone ax.

■ Write a summary of "The Creation of the World".

_____

_____

_____

■ On page 253, complete the cycle showing the creation of the world according to the Chinese myth.

■ In each box, draw a picture of the steps that Pan Koo took to create the world.

■ Write a sentence below each box. The first one has been done for you.

■ Follow the sequence as it was told in the story.

Creation of the World

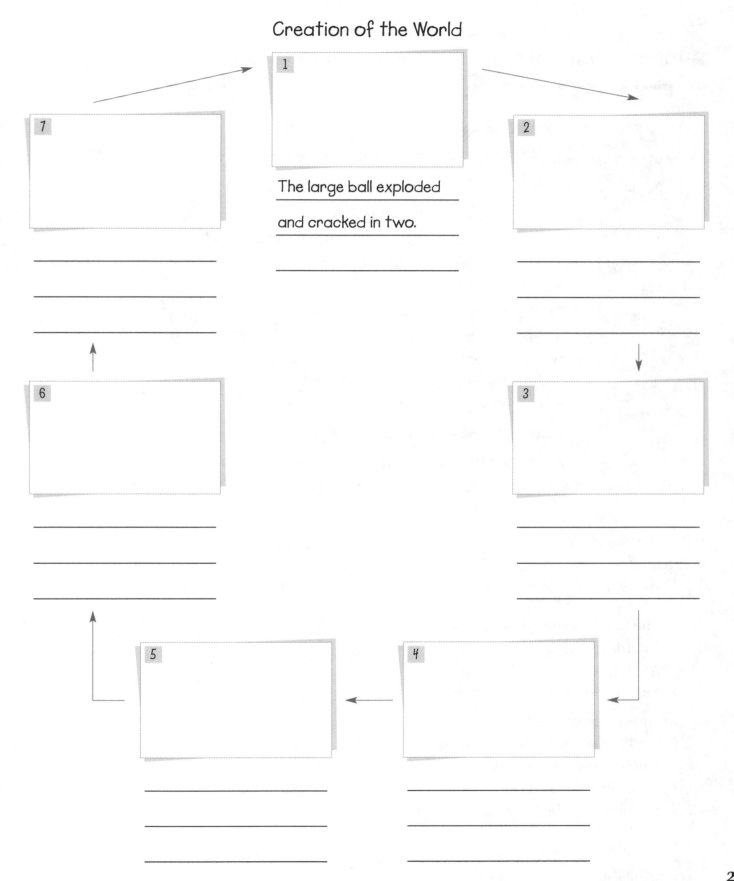

1

The large ball exploded
and cracked in two.

_____

7

_____

_____

_____

2

_____

_____

_____

6

_____

_____

_____

3

_____

_____

_____

5

_____

_____

_____

4

_____

_____

_____

Name _____   Date _____

a Interpreting Information/Facts and Opinions

The Craft Show

All the best crafts will be shown.

When: Saturday, March 10th
Where: Land Park, Sacramento
Cost: Free

■ The following crafts will be exhibited:
Needlepoint and weaving
Homemade dolls
Clay sculptures
Wood crafts

■ Homemade cakes and cookies will be sold.

■ An auction for the exhibited crafts will be held at 5:00 P.M.

1. On the poster, which of these is an opinion?

☐ Needlepoint and weaving will be exhibited.

☐ The craft show will be held on Saturday, March 10th.

☐ All the best crafts will be shown.

☐ The auction will be at 5:00 P.M.

2. This poster doesn't tell you —

☐ the type of crafts that will be exhibited

☐ where the craft show will be held

☐ what time the auction is over

☐ on what day the craft show will be held

3. This poster was written in order to —

☐ tell about the craft show

☐ sell you some crafts

☐ tell you how to do clay sculpture

☐ describe the homemade cookies that will be sold

4. Which type of craft will not be exhibited at the craft show?

☐ needlepoint

☐ wood crafts

☐ clay sculpture

☐ silk painting

254

ELD Standard
Read and orally identify examples of fact/opinion, cause/effect in literature and content-area texts.
ELA Standard
Distinguish facts, supported inferences and opinions in texts.

5. The auction will be at —
   - [ ] 5:00 P.M.
   - [ ] 6:00 P.M.
   - [ ] 7:00 P.M.
   - [ ] 8:30 P.M.

6. On this poster, <u>exhibited</u> means —
   - [ ] encouraged
   - [ ] shown
   - [ ] exiled
   - [ ] cost

7. The items exhibited at the craft show are most likely —
   - [ ] made in a factory by robots
   - [ ] handmade by local artists
   - [ ] made out of plastic
   - [ ] shipped from other countries

Descriptive Writing

Descriptive writing paints a word picture of how something looks.

Writing Prompt

■ Illustrate and describe something that you could display at the craft show.

Before Writing: Think of adjectives to describe the item that you will make for the craft show.

After Writing: Use the writing checklist at the back of the book.

Read the description of the item you will make for the craft show to a partner.

255

Name _____   Date _____

ⓐ Suffixes

▬▬ ▬ ▬▬ ▬▬ ▬▬ ▬▬ ▬▬ ▬▬ ▬▬ ▬▬ ▬▬ ▬▬ ▬▬ ▬

✔ A <u>suffix</u> is a word part that is added to the end of a root word.

✔ A <u>suffix</u> changes the meaning of the root word.

▬▬ ▬ ▬▬ ▬▬ ▬▬ ▬▬ ▬▬ ▬▬ ▬▬ ▬▬ ▬▬ ▬▬ ▬▬ ▬

■ Read the chart on suffixes.

Suffix	Meaning	Example
-er	one who does	*reader* (one who reads)
-able	capable of	*readable* (capable of being read)
-ful	full of	*careful* (full of care)
-less	without	*shoeless* (without shoes)
-y	having, being like	*rainy* (having rain)
-ly	in the manner of	*quickly* (in a quick manner)
-ment	result of	*management* (result of being managed)
-ing	action of; in the process of	*learning* (the act of one that learns)
-ness	condition of, quality, degree of	*fairness* (the condition of being fair)

▬▬ ▬ ▬▬ ▬▬ ▬▬ ▬▬ ▬▬ ▬▬ ▬▬ ▬▬ ▬▬ ▬▬ ▬▬ ▬

■ On page 257, put the cars of the train together to make a word.

■ To do this draw a line between the two train cars that make a word.

■ Write the words that you create on the lines provided. Discuss the meaning of the words you made with a partner.

■ Use each word in a sentence.

ELD Standard
    Spell correctly roots, inflections, suffixes and prefixes and syllable constructions.
ELA Standard
    Spell roots, suffixes, prefixes, contractions and syllable constructions correctly.

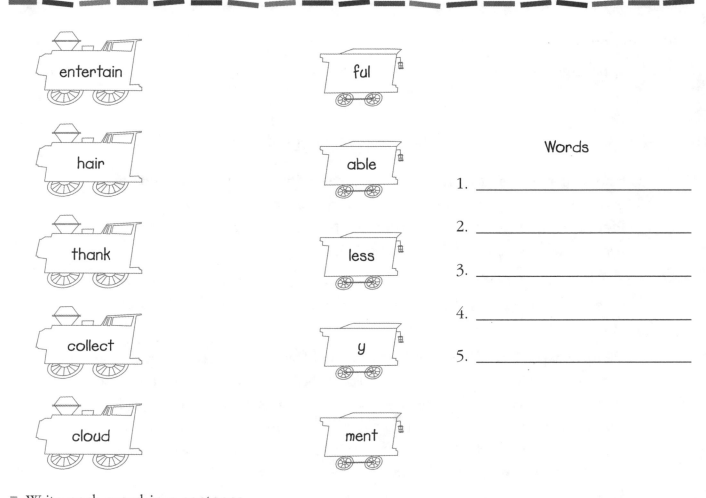

entertain

hair

thank

collect

cloud

ful

able

less

y

ment

Words

1. _____

2. _____

3. _____

4. _____

5. _____

- Write each word in a sentence.
- Read your sentences to a partner.

1. _____

2. _____

3. _____

4. _____

5. _____

Name _____   Date _____

ⓐ Identifying Facts and Opinions

▬ ▬ ▬ ▬ ▬ ▬ ▬ ▬ ▬ ▬ ▬ ▬ ▬ ▬ ▬ ▬ ▬

- Read the questions on page 259 first.
- Read the passage to a partner. Your partner *sums up* the main idea after each paragraph.
- Answer the questions.

The Changing Forest

Have you ever been to a forest? Some trees in the forest are hundreds of years old. These ancient trees have probably seen a lot of changes in the forest. Can you imagine what an old pine tree might tell you about how the forest has changed over the last hundred years?

Flora is a pine tree that has lived in the forest for the last hundred years. This is her story about how the forest has changed from years past through the present.

"Hi, my name is Flora. I have lived in this forest for over 100 years. I have seen a lot of changes here. I've seen the animals that used to live in the forest move away. The meadow mice moved because their food supply was gone and there was no more grass for them to build their nests. White-footed mice took their place. They made their nests in hollow stumps and logs. They ate seeds from the trees and shrubs. For the first time, deer came to live on the land. Now there were places for them to hide and tender shoots for them to eat.

"Cardinals came and perched in the trees. So did redstarts, ovenbirds and ruffed grouse. Squirrels and chipmunks brought nuts onto the land. Some of these sprouted with the other seedlings.

"One summer afternoon fifty years ago, a storm broke out over the land. Lightning struck the tallest pines, killing some of them and damaging others. Strong winds uprooted more pines and lightning fires scorched branches.

"But this is how forests grow. The death of some of the pine trees made room for the growth of new and different trees that had been sprouting on the

ELD Standard
  Read and orally identify examples of fact/opinion, cause/effect in literature and content-area texts.
ELA Standard
  Draw inferences, conclusions, or generalizations about text and support them with textual evidence and prior knowledge.

forest floor. As time passed, insects and disease hurt the other pines. Every time one of them died, a red oak, white ash or red maple tree took its place.

"The forest grew. By the year 1860, the pioneer white pines were nearly all gone. Red oaks, red maples and ash trees were everywhere. The forest had grown and changed again. The red oaks were the prettiest trees in the forest."

1. There is enough information in this passage to show that —
   - ☐ the lightning never struck the forest
   - ☐ the forest changed over the years
   - ☐ the red oaks were the tallest trees
   - ☐ Flora is the oldest tree in the forest

2. In this article, which of the following is an opinion?
   - ☐ Cardinals perched in the trees.
   - ☐ The red oaks were the prettiest trees in the forest.
   - ☐ The forest grew.
   - ☐ The pioneer white pines were nearly all gone.

3. Which of the following lines does the writer provide to support the claim that the forest changed?
   - ☐ White-footed mice ate seeds from the trees and shrubs.
   - ☐ The animals that used to live in the forest moved away.
   - ☐ Flora lived in the forest for 100 years.
   - ☐ There were ancient trees in the forest.

4. The author of this passage probably believes that —
   - ☐ change is good because it allows for new growth
   - ☐ all change is bad
   - ☐ pine trees are ugly
   - ☐ the forest would be better if it had never changed

5. What would happen if a large carnivore, or meat-eating animal, were introduced to this forest?
   - ☐ the number of trees would decrease
   - ☐ the number of deer would decrease
   - ☐ the number of meadow mice would increase
   - ☐ white pines would grow again

6. What will happen to the forest in the future?
   - ☐ the forest will continue to change
   - ☐ people will cut down all the trees
   - ☐ white-footed mice will live there forever
   - ☐ no new trees will grow there

Name _____   Date _____

b Interpreting Graphs

- Write a summary explaining this bar graph.
- Answer the questions:

How many trees grew in the forest each year?
Why do you think there were more trees during certain years?

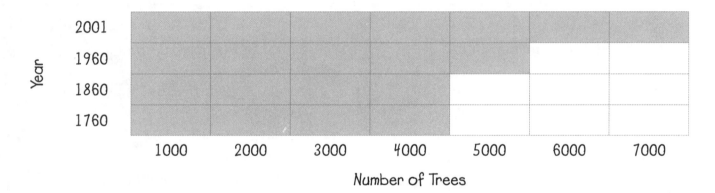

Tree Growth in the Forest

Bar Graph Summary

_____

_____

_____

_____

_____

_____

ELD Standard
    Read and orally identify examples of fact/opinion, cause/effect in literature and content–area texts.
ELA Standard
    Understand how text features (e.g. format, graphics, sequence, diagrams and illustrations) make information accessible and usable.

Name _____   Date _____

ⓐ Identifying and Correctly Using Verbs

✔ There are some verbs that are often misused. Two of these verbs are *lie* and *lay*.

■ Read the verb forms of *lay* and *lie* in the two note pads below.

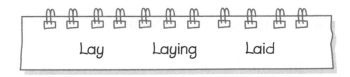

Lay   Laying   Laid

✔ The verb *lay* is used for putting an object down.

Please *lay* this on the table.
She is *laying* the book down.
John *laid* it there yesterday.

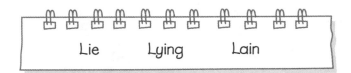

Lie   Lying   Lain

✔ The verb *lie* is used for the physical act of lying down.

The baby *lies* in his cradle.
He has been *lying* there for an hour.
Has she *lain* there long?

ELD Standard
    Use correct parts of speech.
ELA Standard
    Identify and correctly use verbs that are often misused (lie/lay, sit/set, rise/raise), pronouns, and modifiers.

lay, lays, laying, laid
lie, lies, lying, lain

■ Write the correct verb from the notepad in each sentence. Read the sentences to a partner.

1. My brother has been _____ there for an hour.

2. Has my sister _____ there for a long time?

3. My father was _____ on the grass.

4. "Mary, please _____ the book about family trees on this desk," said Joe.

5. My aunt is _____ the tablecloth on the table.

6. My uncle _____ the magazine on the counter yesterday.

7. Where has your niece _____ her pencils?

8. Has his daughter _____ the pencils under the papers?

9. How long has the pet dog _____ there?

10. My grandfather is _____ on the sofa.

Name _____   Date _____

a Demonstrating Comprehension

- Read the questions on page 264 first.
- Read the passage to a partner. Your partner *sums up* the main idea after each paragraph. Switch roles.
- Answer the questions.

Future School Building Designs
Architecture for the Future

If you would like to submit a design for a school building of the future, read the following information:

1. You must be fifteen to twenty years old.

2. Your design must be original and three-dimensional. It can be made of wood, paper or clay.

3. When you send in your future school building design, include a label with your name on it.

4. If you are interested in seeing other people's designs, look on our website at www.futuremagazine.net.

5. Please include a self-addressed envelope if you would like to receive a list of the winners of the contest.

6. The best future school building design will be featured in *Future Magazine* in May. If your design is featured, you will receive three free copies of the magazine.

7. Send all entries to:
   Future School Building Designs
   1714 West Road
   Chicago, Illinois 68910

ELD Standard
 Orally identify basic sequence of written text using simple sentences.
ELA Standard
 Read aloud narrative and expository text fluently and accurately.

263

1. Designs that are sent in must be —
   - ☐ 8" x 12"
   - ☐ entered on the Internet
   - ☐ three-dimensional
   - ☐ made of clay only

2. When will the best future school building design be featured in *Future Magazine*?
   - ☐ May
   - ☐ June
   - ☐ July
   - ☐ September

3. These directions are written in order to —
   - ☐ sell a magazine
   - ☐ tell how to design a future school building
   - ☐ give guidelines
   - ☐ tell how to build a space home

4. Whoever's design is chosen as best will receive —
   - ☐ three free copies of *Future Magazine*
   - ☐ one hundred dollars
   - ☐ two copies of School Building Design
   - ☐ a self-addressed envelope

5. Which of these materials can the three-dimensional design not be made of?
   - ☐ paper
   - ☐ metal
   - ☐ clay
   - ☐ wood

6. Designs that are sent in must be —
   - ☐ made of clay
   - ☐ old
   - ☐ made of wood
   - ☐ original

7. What would probably happen if you submit a design made of metal?
   - ☐ Your entry might win first prize.
   - ☐ Your entry might be featured on the magazine's website.
   - ☐ You might receive three free copies of the magazine.
   - ☐ Your entry might be disqualified.

8. Of the four entries below, which design would most likely win the contest?
   - ☐ a school design with flying chalkboards in each classroom
   - ☐ a school design with a cafeteria that serves delicious food
   - ☐ a school design with electric fences protecting the students
   - ☐ a school design with colorful lockers at the school's entrance

Name _____   Date _____

ⓑ Descriptive Writing

— —

Descriptive Writing

✔ Descriptive writing describes how something looks, smells, tastes, feels or sounds.

— —

Writing Prompt

- Design and draw a school building for the future.
  On the lines below, describe why you created the school building to look a certain way.
  On a separate sheet of paper, describe what activities people perform in the school building.

_____

_____

_____

_____

ELD Standard
Begin to use a variety of genres in writing.
ELA Standard
Write narrative expository and descriptive texts.

265

Name   Date

a Interpreting Facts and Opinions

- Read the questions on page 267 first.
- Read the advertisement to a partner. Your partner retells the main idea. Switch roles.
- Answer the questions.

Comfy Jackets
Stay Warm in Our Jackets

Stay warm in our insulated jackets. We sell the best jackets on the market.

Why do people love to wear our jackets?
- ✔ The jackets are insulated to keep you warm.
- ✔ They come in many styles.
- ✔ Most of all, they are comfortable and warm.

At **Comfy Jackets Inc.**, we make jackets that will keep you warm and dry even if you get caught in the rain.

- ■ Our process of coating the jacket with silicone waterproofs the jacket.
- ■ Our jackets are also sturdy.
- ■ We double-stitch the seams to prevent tears.

Wear a **Comfy Jacket!**
Available in Small, Medium and Large for $99.00

ELD Standard
Read and orally identify examples of fact/opinion, cause/effect in literature and content-area texts.
ELA Standard
Distinguish facts, supported inferences and opinions in texts.

1. What does the manufacturer do to waterproof the jackets?
   - [ ] They sew them carefully.
   - [ ] They put them in the dryer before selling them.
   - [ ] They coat them with silicone.
   - [ ] They wear them in the rain before selling them.

2. Comfy Jackets are double-stitched to make them —
   - [ ] comfortable
   - [ ] adjustable
   - [ ] sturdy
   - [ ] wet

3. This Comfy Jacket ad stresses the company's —
   - [ ] reasonable prices and flexible hours
   - [ ] warm sturdy jackets that are durable
   - [ ] variety of items
   - [ ] friendly salespeople

4. In this Comfy Jacket ad, which of these is an opinion?
   - [ ] We sell the best jackets on the market.
   - [ ] Comfy Jackets sell for $99.00.
   - [ ] The jackets are insulated.
   - [ ] The jackets come in many styles.

5. You would most likely find this ad in a —
   - [ ] sewing book
   - [ ] sports book
   - [ ] fashion magazine
   - [ ] science book

- In the space below, write your own advertisement. Illustrate it.

- Use words and pictures that will make people want to buy your product.

Name   Date

ⓐ Interpreting Expository Writing

- Read the questions on page 269 first.
- Read the advertisements on pages 268 and 269 to a partner. Your partner *sums up* the main idea of each advertisement. Switch roles.
- Answer the questions.

Electro

Don't pay for Gas!

Drive an Electric Car

We Sell the Most Economical Car on the Market

Why do people love to drive electric cars?

The answer is simple. Electric cars are cheaper to drive.

At Electro Car Company, we make electric cars with the best computerized engine in the world. The computerized engine is made to keep the price of the Electro reasonable. Electro cars come in many styles and colors. Electro cars start at less than $20,000.

Buy an Electro Car!

Electro Cars are Available at Car Dealerships Across the Country.

268

ELD Standard
    Read and orally identify examples of fact/opinion, cause/effect in literature and content-area texts.
ELA Standard
    Distinguish facts, supported inferences and opinions in texts.

Charger
The Charge Electric Cars are the Most Reliable Cars in the World!

Our Cars Come in Different Sizes.
We Have Economy and Luxury Models.
Everyone would love to save money on gas.
Think of the things you could buy with the money you save.

The Charger Car offers you many advantages.

✔ We offer the best electric car on the market.
✔ Our cars only need to be charged every three months.
✔ We offer 0% financing over three years.
✔ You get a free gold insignia on all new Chargers.
✔ Chargers start at just $25,000.

Wherever You Like to Drive, You'll Love Driving the Charger. The Charger is the Most Reliable and Economical Car on the Market.

1. In the Electro car ad, the words "on the market" mean —
   - ☐ at sale price
   - ☐ for sale anywhere
   - ☐ ever made
   - ☐ for sale only in designated towns

2. Which of these is an opinion in the Charger car ad?
   - ☐ We offer a rebate of $1,000.
   - ☐ You get a free gold insignia.
   - ☐ We offer 0% financing over three years.
   - ☐ We offer the best electric car on the market.

3. You would most likely find these ads in a —
   - ☐ newspaper
   - ☐ history book
   - ☐ sports magazine
   - ☐ furniture catalog

4. The Electro car ad stresses that —
   - ☐ the car comes with 0% financing
   - ☐ the car comes with a rebate
   - ☐ the car is economical
   - ☐ the car is made of sturdy plastic

5. The Charger needs to be charged ---
   - ☐ once a month
   - ☐ every three months
   - ☐ every four months
   - ☐ every week

6. Electro cars have a computerized engine to make them —
   - ☐ more like cars that use gas
   - ☐ more sleek
   - ☐ more sturdy
   - ☐ more economical

Name _____   Date _____

b Expository Writing

━ ━ ━ ━ ━ ━ ━ ━ ━ ━ ━ ━ ━ ━ ━ ━ ━ ━

✔ Expository writing gives information.

It can be in the form of an advertisement.

━ ━ ━ ━ ━ ━ ━ ━ ━ ━ ━ ━ ━ ━ ━ ━ ━ ━

Writing Prompt

▪ Compare and contrast the Electro and Charger using the compare and contrast mind map below.

On page 271, write about which car you would buy and why.

Design your own ad for an electric car.

List the advantages of the car you design.

Draw a picture of your electric car.

Before Writing: Complete the mind map below.

After Writing: Use the writing checklist at the end of the book.

Have a partner use the writing checklist to edit your writing.

Read what you wrote to a partner.

Compare and Contrast

Electro and Charge

How are these two things different?	How are these two things the same?
▪	▪
▪	▪
▪	▪
▪	▪

270

ELD Standard
Begin to use a variety of genres in writing.
ELA Standard
Write narrative expository and descriptive texts.

I would like to buy the

_____

_____

_____

_____

- Write an ad for an electric car on the lines below.
- Draw a picture of your electric car.

Name   Date

a Interpreting Fact and Opinion

✔ Sometimes opinions are clearly opinions.

My mom makes the best spaghetti and meatballs in the world.

✔ Sometimes opinions look like facts. Beware!

Pilots say that it is safer to fly on Pajaro Airways than on Pichoncito Airlines.
Cooking in convection ovens makes your food more delicious.

✔ The people who write these "facts" want you to believe what they write.

✔ They do not support their arguments with statistics.

✔ They make these "facts" look authoritative.

■ Read the questions on pages 273 and 274 first.

■ Read the passage to a partner. Your partner *sums up* the main idea after each paragraph. Switch roles.

■ Answer the questions.

Microwave Ovens

Have you ever used a microwave oven? Chefs all over the world say that microwave ovens have revolutionized kitchens! Microwave ovens cook much faster than regular ovens. Unlike ordinary ovens that use gas or electric heat, a microwave oven uses microwaves to heat, defrost or cook food. Microwaves are produced when electricity is passed through a device called a *magnetron*.

Food in a microwave oven cooks faster because the waves penetrating the food heat it from the inside out, as well as from the outside in. Microwaves heat the molecules of water in the food, cooking the food evenly and thoroughly. Just like in a regular oven, some foods take more time than others to cook in a microwave. Warming up soup may take two minutes while cooking a chicken may take fifteen to twenty minutes. An ordinary oven takes longer to cook food. A chicken may take an hour or more to cook in a regular oven. Microwaves cook the best food you've ever tasted.

ELD Standard
   Read and orally identify examples of fact/opinion, cause/effect in literature and content-area texts.
ELA Standard
   Distinguish facts, supported inferences and opinions in texts.

Microwave cooking has another advantage over oven cooking. An oven cooks the food from the outside in. This is why chicken can be brown on the outside but still be undercooked on the inside. The microwave cooks food both from the outside in and from the inside out. Therefore, food cooked for the correct number of minutes in a microwave is always cooked well.

There are some disadvantages to using the microwave. One disadvantage is that you cannot use metal containers or tin foil for cooking. This is because microwaves cannot pass through metal. It is best to use plastic or glass containers when cooking in a microwave.

1. There is enough information in this article to show that —
   - ☐ microwave ovens are expensive
   - ☐ microwave ovens cook faster than regular ovens
   - ☐ microwave ovens cook tastier food than regular ovens
   - ☐ microwave ovens are white or beige

2. Another good name for this story is —
   - ☐ Regular Ovens
   - ☐ The Fast Cooking Oven
   - ☐ The Best Recipe
   - ☐ Cooking at the River Park

3. Why did the author begin this article with a question?
   - ☐ to persuade the reader to buy a microwave oven
   - ☐ to get the reader to relate the article to his or her experience
   - ☐ to tell how to clean a microwave
   - ☐ to outline the uses of a microwave

4. In this article, which of these is an <u>opinion</u>?
   - ☐ Microwave ovens cook faster than regular ovens.
   - ☐ You cannot use metal containers in microwave ovens.
   - ☐ Microwave ovens heat the molecules of water in the food.
   - ☐ Microwaves cook the best food you've ever tasted.

5 What is another opinion in this article?
   - ☐ Chefs all over the world say that microwave ovens have revolutionized kitchens!
   - ☐ Microwaves are produced when electricity is passed through a device called a magnetron.
   - ☐ An oven cooks the food from the outside in.
   - ☐ You cannot use metal containers or tin foil for cooking.

6. This article is most like —
- ☐ a biography
- ☐ an advertisement
- ☐ a history lesson
- ☐ a legend

7. All the following are facts about a microwave <u>except</u> —
- ☐ microwaves ovens cook food faster than regular ovens
- ☐ microwaves cook food from the outside in and from the inside out
- ☐ you can use tin foil to cover food in the microwave
- ☐ microwave ovens use microwaves to heat, defrost and cook food

■ Write a comparison of the regular oven and the microwave oven including advantages and disadvantages of each oven.

Regular Oven	
Advantages	Disadvantages
_____	_____
_____	_____
_____	_____

Microwave Oven	
Advantages	Disadvantages
_____	_____
_____	_____
_____	_____

Name _____   Date _____

ⓐ Interpreting a Persuasive Paragraph

- -

Outline of Elements of a Persuasive Paragraph

I.	Topic	Choose a topic you believe in.
II.	Opinion	Write a topic sentence that supports your opinion.
III.	Reasons	Give reasons to support your opinion.
IV.	Evidence or Facts	Give facts to help persuade the reader that your opinion is valid.
V.	Conclusion	Write a persuasive conclusion to convince others to think like you do.

- -

Writing Prompt

▪ On a separate sheet of paper, write a persuasive paragraph on the best form of communication (telephone, radio, TV, Internet, etc.).

Before Writing: Follow the outline of elements for a persuasive paragraph. Start your outline below.

After Writing: Use the writing checklist at the back of the book to edit your work. Read your paragraph to a partner.

The Best Form of Communication

_____

_____

_____

_____

_____

ELD Standard
    Write a persuasive composition using standard grammatical forms.
ELA Standard
    Write persuasive letters or compositions. Support a position with relevant evidence. Follow a simple organizational pattern.

Name   Date
_____   _____

▣ Demonstrating Comprehension

▬▬ ▬▬ ▬▬ ▬▬ ▬▬ ▬▬ ▬▬ ▬▬ ▬▬ ▬▬ ▬▬ ▬▬ ▬▬ ▬▬ ▬▬

- Read the questions on page 277 first.
- Read the passage to a partner. Your partner *sums up* the main idea after each paragraph. Switch roles.
- Answer the questions.

Bill Melendez and the Art of Animation

(1)   Have you ever heard of Bill Melendez? Bill Melendez has a very exciting career. He is a cartoon animator. The job of a cartoon animator is to create the movement for cartoon characters.

(2)   In the past, animators used a series of drawings to create a cartoon character's movements. The drawings were made up of lines, circles and colors on a piece of paper. The cartoon characters couldn't move on their own, but the animator made them appear to move. Good animators made the movements look smooth and natural. Mickey Mouse, Charlie Brown and Popeye couldn't really move but they appeared to be moving in cartoons. The animator drew Charlie Brown's movements very realistically. Charlie Brown not only moved but he had expressions on his face. Bill Melendez is an animator who drew cartoon characters' movements. Charlie Brown, Lucy and Mickey Mouse are a few of the cartoon characters that Bill Melendez has animated.

(3)   Bill Melendez has done animation for forty-five years. His first employer was Walt Disney Studios. Bill was hired as an assistant animator for Mickey Mouse and Donald Duck cartoons. He also worked on the films *Dumbo* and *Fantasia*.

ELD Standard
  Read and orally identify the main ideas and use them to draw inferences about written text using simple sentences.
ELA Standard
  Draw inferences, conclusions or generalizations and support them with textual evidence and prior knowledge.

(4)   Bill Melendez never intended to be an animator. Bill explains, "After I finished school, I needed a job. Disney Studios had lots of jobs for animators. They were hiring anyone who could draw a circle or a straight line. I figured I knew how to doodle pretty well. I liked to draw. I took the job at the Disney Studios because I thought it would be a fun job. I learned animation by watching the people around me. I learned the art of animation from mentors at the Disney Studios."

(5)   Technology has changed the job of an animator. Today, animation is done on a computer. Computer programs <u>facilitate</u> the process of getting cartoon characters to run, smile and play baseball.

1. This story is mainly about —
   ☐ computerized animation
   ☐ Bill Melendez
   ☐ Charlie Brown
   ☐ Mickey Mouse

2. What does an animator <u>not</u> do?
   ☐ draw lines and squares
   ☐ draw pictures that seem to move
   ☐ make cartoon characters move
   ☐ write movies the cartoon characters

3. This is a true story about Bill Melendez. That means it is —
   ☐ fiction
   ☐ non-fiction
   ☐ science fiction
   ☐ historical fiction

4. In paragraph 5 of this passage, the word <u>facilitate</u> means —
   ☐ to make more difficult
   ☐ a place to live
   ☐ to make easier
   ☐ to become less expensive

5. This story is most like —
   ☐ a legend
   ☐ a biography
   ☐ an advertisement
   ☐ a history lesson

6. To learn more about Bill Melendez, you should —
   ☐ visit an amusement park
   ☐ read his biography
   ☐ look in the dictionary under cartoons
   ☐ look in a recipe book

Name   Date

b Narrative Writing

Narrative Writing

✔ Narrative writing tells a story.

Writing Prompt

■ Draw a cartoon.
Write a story about what the characters are doing in the cartoon.

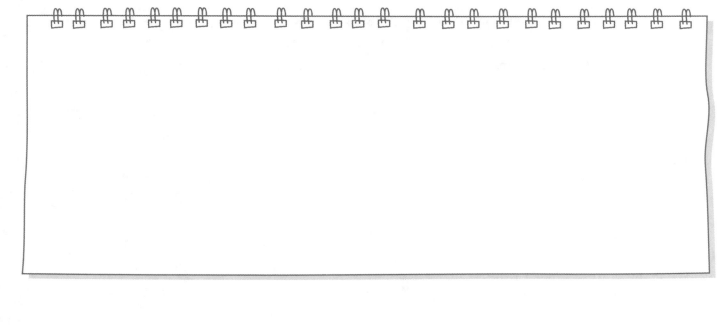

ELD Standard
Write short narrative stories include elements of setting and character.
ELA Standard
Write narratives. Establish a plot, point of view and setting.

Name _____   Date _____

a Using Adverbs

- ✔ An <u>adverb</u> is a word that describes a verb.

- ✔ Adverbs tell *how, when* or *where.*

  I run *quickly* to school. (how)

  I *never* watch TV during dinner. (when)

  My computer is *here.* (where)

- ✔ Many adverbs end in *-ly.* These simple adverbs modify the verb.

- ▪ Underline the verb and adverb in each sentence.
- ▪ Write the adverb on the line that follows each sentence.
- ▪ Read the sentences to a partner.

  Example: I <u>run quickly.</u>

  1. Martha reads books regularly.   _____

  2. Mike completed the report on his computer successfully.   _____

  3. Carlos talks loudly at the movies.   _____

  4. Please turn the radio volume down quickly.   _____

  5. I read the rules for the video game carefully.   _____

  6. The lady walked slowly down the theater aisle.   _____

  7. It seldom snows in Atlanta.   _____

  8. I won the computer game easily.   _____

  9. My dad drives slowly in the rain.   _____

  10. My mom communicates with Grandma regularly over the Internet.   _____

ELD Standard
   Use parts of speech correctly.
ELA Standard
   Identify and correctly use verbs that are often misused, modifiers and pronouns.

Name _____   Date _____

a Interpreting Facts and Opinions/Demonstrating Comprehension

■ Read the questions on pages 281 and 282 first.

■ Read the passage to a partner. Your partner *sums up* the main idea after each paragraph. Switch roles.

■ Answer the questions.

Internet Student Banking

(1)   Do you earn money by raking lawns or helping to clean the house? Have you participated in a car wash or a yard sale to earn money? Many students want to save the money they earn to buy something special like a new bike or to go on a special trip. Some students want to save their money for college.

(2)   Where do you save your money? Grandpa used to save his money in an old coffee can. Then he'd bury the can in the garden. Sometimes, when it rained a lot, he ended up with a lot of soggy money. Aunt Sara used to save her money in a big, poodle-shaped piggy bank. When the felt-covered poodle was full, she had no alternative but to crack it open. Aunt Sara was always unhappy when she had to destroy the piggy bank to get her money.

(3)   Mama had a better idea. She saved her money in the bank. She established an account and then put her money in the bank. Mama kept a bankbook. The bankbook gave her the balance of the money she had in the bank. Mama was delighted when she saw her balance continue to grow.

(4)   Now there's a new way banking technology that Grandpa, Aunt Sara and Mama didn't have. It is called Internet banking. Internet banking allows you to establish a bank account using your computer. You can log onto your bank's website and give them your confidential information including your social security number, your birth date and your mother's maiden name. The bank will then ask you to type in a secret code. Your secret code can be made up of letters or numbers. The secret code is used by you to access your bank account.

ELD Standard
Read and orally identify examples of fact/opinion, cause/effect in literature and content area texts.
ELA Standard
Distinguish facts, supported inferences and opinions in text.

(5)   There are three kinds of accounts that you can establish over the Internet. One type of an account is a savings account. A savings account earns money called <u>interest</u>. The second type of account is called a checking account. A checking account enables you to write out a check when you decide to purchase something. This means that you can go to the store without cash. The store sends your check to the bank. The money is <u>debited</u> from your checking account. Only students over twelve years old can have a checking account. Most checking accounts don't give you interest on your money. The third type of account is a money market account. Some money market accounts pay more interest than a savings account but you must keep your money in the account for at least a year.

(6)   Internet banking offers you more than just tools for online banking. It enables you to log onto a banking resource hub so that you can learn more about how to invest your money for the future. At the resource hub, there are videos you can watch online. You can watch these videos again and again. You can also order books online.

(7)   It is important for students to learn how to save and invest their money so that they have more for the future. Saving money is the most efficient way to become a young millionaire.

---

1. All these are types of bank accounts you can establish on the Internet except for —
   - ☐ money market debit accounts
   - ☐ savings accounts
   - ☐ money market accounts
   - ☐ checking accounts

2. In this article, which of these is an <u>opinion</u>?
   - ☐ There is a banking resource hub.
   - ☐ There are three types of Internet accounts.
   - ☐ Internet banking allows you to establish a bank account over the Internet.
   - ☐ Saving money is the most efficient way to become a young millionaire.

3. The boxes show some ideas discussed in the article.

```
                        ┌─────────────────────────────┐
                        │   Internet Student Banking   │
                        └─────────────────────────────┘
   ┌──────────────┐  ┌─────────────────────┐  ┌──────────────────────┐  ┌──────────────────┐
   │ Savings      │  │ Money Market        │  │ Banking Resource Hub │  │ Checking Account │
   │ Account      │  │ Account             │  │                      │  │                  │
   └──────────────┘  └─────────────────────┘  └──────────────────────┘  └──────────────────┘
                          ┌──────────────────┐  ┌──────────────────┐
                          │   Videos Online  │  │                  │
                          └──────────────────┘  └──────────────────┘
```

Which of these belongs in the empty box?
- ☐ travel logs
- ☐ order books online
- ☐ calculator
- ☐ order a pass book

4. If you want to open an Internet checking account, you must be at least —
- ☐ ten years old
- ☐ twelve years old
- ☐ thirteen years old
- ☐ sixteen years old

5. Why did the author begin this article with a question?
- ☐ to give directions
- ☐ to explain how to become a millionaire
- ☐ to persuade the reader to buy a product
- ☐ to get the reader interested in reading the article

6. In paragraph 5, <u>debited</u> means —
- ☐ taken out
- ☐ put in
- ☐ gave money back
- ☐ started a money market account

▬ ▬

■ Write a short summary of the passage. Use a thesaurus to help you.

_____

_____

_____

Writing Checklist / Peer Editing

Example

Prewriting: Things to do before writing	
Choose a topic.	
Brainstorm. Use one or more of these graphic organizers: list, outline, table, graph, diagram, story map, mind map.	

Drafting: The first version of your work	
Choose and sequence your ideas. Use your graphic organizers.	
Write a first draft.	

Revising: Improving your work	
Read over what you wrote. Does it make sense? Does a word need to be added or taken out?	
Make sure each sentence has a noun (person, place, or thing).	The *building* is very tall.
Make sure each sentence has a verb (action word).	The president *travels* frequently.
Make sure the subject and the verb of each sentence agree. If a subject ends in "s," the verb can't end in "s."	*My friends play* computer games.
Pay careful attention to the verb tense.	*Yesterday,* I *waited* for you.
Use plurals correctly.	book*s*, speech*es*, cact*i*
Use a variety of parts of speech (adverbs, adjectives, etc.).	The *tall, handsome* man with the *big, red* hat walked *quickly* away.
Expressions and idioms are not changed.	*It's raining cats and dogs.*
Only one *and* or *but* is allowed in a single sentence.	She is going to play *and* go swimming. I like math, *but* my brother likes science.

Proofreading: Correcting spelling, punctuation and grammatical mistakes	
Always capitalize the word *I*.	<u>I</u> like to eat soup. Maria and <u>I</u> look alike.
Check to see that each sentence begins with a capital letter.	<u>Y</u>our brother reads the newspaper.
Check to see that each sentence ends with the correct punctuation (.!?): ▪ A period ends a statement. ▪ A question mark ends a question. ▪ An exclamation point ends a sentence that expresses strong emotion.	We are going skating<u>.</u> What's your address<u>?</u> Wow, this is fun<u>!</u>
Check to see that each new idea begins a new paragraph. Indent each new paragraph. If your writing has more than one paragraph, you can indent each new paragraph or skip a line between each paragraph.	
Check the spelling of frequently misspelled words (such as *their*, *they're*, *there* and *two*, *to*, *too*): ▪ Incorrect: I speak English. I speak Spanish, to. ▪ Correct: I speak English. I speak Spanish, too.	
Check the spelling of contractions.	will not = won't; should not = shouldn't; would not = wouldn't; must not = mustn't; can not = can't; could not = couldn't; it is = it's; they are = they're
Check to see that commas are used correctly. ▪ Use a comma between the name of a city and a state. ▪ Use a comma between the day and the year in a date. ▪ Use a comma to separate three or more items in a series.	He lives in Fresno<u>,</u> California. My younger sister was born on August 14<u>,</u> 1995. She likes cats<u>,</u> dogs and mice.

Publishing: Presenting your work to the world	
Copy over your story neatly.	
Have a partner edit your story using the Writing Checklist.	
Read your final story to a partner.	

Program Philosophy

Each and every one of the educators, authors, editors, and designers who created

McGraw-Hill's Adventures in Time and Place share a deep commitment to provide

- **rich, relevant content** in all areas of social studies at every grade level
- **geographic literacy skills** for all students, created in partnership with the National Geographic Society
- **easy-to-use teaching materials** with choices to accommodate diverse student learning styles and support various teaching styles

Program Authorship

National Geographic Society, the world's premier authority on

NATIONAL GEOGRAPHIC SOCIETY geography and

geography education, joins the same team that created the best-selling McGraw-Hill Social Studies Program

THE WORLD AROUND US to bring you a brand new program...

Adventures in Time and Place.

DR. BARRY BEYER
George Mason University
Fairfax, VA

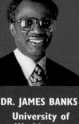

DR. JAMES BANKS
University of Washington
Seattle, WA

JEAN CRAVEN
Albuquerque Public Schools
Albuquerque, NM

DR. GLORIA CONTRERAS
University of North Texas
Denton, TX

DR. MARY MCFARLAND
Parkway Public Schools
Creve Coeur, MO

DR. WALTER PARKER
University of Washington
Seattle, WA

DR. GLORIA LADSON-BILLINGS
University of Wisconsin-Madison
Madison, WI

Choices in easy-to-use materials

6 theme big books for group instruction

UNIT 1 THEME BIG BOOK WHERE WE LIVE

My World
ADVENTURES IN TIME AND PLACE

My World
ADVENTURES IN TIME AND PLACE

A Pupil Edition for individual teaching

GRADES K–2

You have these options to choose from:

- Teach with Big Books (K–2)
- Teach with Pupil Edition (1–2)
- Teach with a combination (1–2)

Use the same manageable Teacher's Edition for all three options. Choose the activities that meet your needs, in your setting, to fit your classroom style!

A Teacher's Multimedia Edition to support your approach

Activities provide options for hands-on learning

Choices help you meet your needs and reach your goals

AT EVERY GRADE

The rich content is supported by hands-on activities and brought to life through motivating primary sources and diverse perspectives. Your teaching is supported with a 3-Step Lesson Plan — 1 PREPARE, 2 TEACH, 3 CLOSE — that's easy to use and easy to manage.